Illusions

Edited by

EDI LANNERS

Translated and adapted

by Heinz Norden

Holt, Rinehart and Winston · New York

ABOUT THIS BOOK

Only a few decades ago, we still believed science could explain the 'how' of everything. Today we face the question of whether we are even in touch with reality, or ever can be. Thinkers and philosophers have become convinced that the objects of our world merely represent the sum of their properties for us and that these qualities exist solely in our consciousness. What we perceive is the result of a thinking process, a kind of natural magic, that conjures up within us a sensation of the object seen, while at the same time suggesting to us a belief in its reality. Perhaps the greatest illusion is the way we take it for granted that the real world 'out there' coincides with what we optically perceive as 'real'. The image we create of our environment is purely human and subjective, hence one-sided. A dog's image of the world, or that of a bee or a bird, is quite different. Every living creature is equipped with different organs, receives impressions altogether different from ours, and these images are integrated in utterly different fashion, in the differently organized brains nature has provided. Everyone really feels, hears, sees only in his brain, in his own peculiar and mysterious fashion. Oddly enough, we tend to give little thought to the machinery with which we think and feel, build up our lives, create our view of the world, take our decisions. We fail to appreciate that this machinery not only remains an unsolved puzzle, but all too often succumbs to error, is swayed by prejudice, gives way to illusions. Is illusion merely a superficial represent- ation of the world, just a figment in practical life? Or is it an amusing form of self-deception that takes the place of a sober look at the facts? When we critically examine the 'mechanism' of illusion, the in- sight we thus gain into our weaknesses, rather than 'disillusion' us, is likely to exert a certain fascination, especially when we come to realize that de- spite our awareness that we are victims of illusion, we are unable to avoid suc- cumbing to it. Illusion, further- more, need not be considered solely as deception and falsification, for it represents at the same time the fundamental creative principle, the motive that impels us to change the world along the lines of our dreams. Hence delving into illusion and error is more than merely entertaining. It may stimulate us to engage in original reflection and fruitful meditation.

Contents

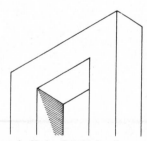

Copyright © 1973 by Verlag C. J. Bucher, Luzern and Frankfurt/M
English translation copyright © 1977 Thames and Hudson Ltd., London
First published in the United States in 1977 by Holt, Rinehart and Winston

Library of Congress Catalog Card Number: 77–71375

ISBN: Hardbound 0–03–020891–2
Paperback 0–03–020886–6

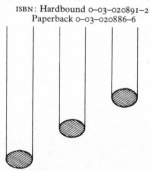

PRINTED IN GREAT BRITAIN

Light, colour, heat and the like, as well as configuration, dimension and movement, merely appear to be qualities.

LEIBNIZ

Man is the shadow of a dream.

PINDAR

A Spartan was plucking a nightingale and found very little meat. Thou art a voice, he cried out, and nothing else besides.

AFTER PLUTARCH

When Thales of Miletus was asked how wide was the gulf between the truth and a lie, he said: As wide as that betwixt eye and ear.

AFTER STOBAEUS

The eyes of nocturnal birds are useless in clear daylight. So too our insight fails in the face of things that are by nature the clearest of all.

ARISTOTLE

For now we see through a glass, darkly; but then face to face: now I know in part; but then shall I know even as also I am known.

I CORINTHIANS 13:12

Everyday Illusion

by Walter Robert Corti

An error recognized as such is corrected and thus resolved. An illusion recognized as such, on the other hand, remains an illusion and fools us again the very next moment. We have known ever since Copernicus that the sun does not 'rise' above the horizon in the morning – but still it rises. We do not experience what we know, and our knowledge has a hard time teaching our experience. This is supremely true of the proposition that we are able to recognize our concepts only within ourselves. We may realize it a thousand times over, yet time and again we succumb to everyday illusion.

I am seated in my study, see the table before me, the bookshelves along the walls, the cat sleeping on the armchair, the dark fir tree against the blue sky outside the window. I quite believe that I perceive all these things *outside* before me in space. This is an illusion. I do not mean to dispute the existence of space out there, but I do not see it. Our eyes form two small globes, like large marbles children play with, just under an inch in diameter. They are open in front, and as in a camera, the iris can increase or reduce the aperture. The outside world is projected on the spherically curved retina inside. We say that we look out into the world with our eyes. Actually, the opposite is true. Through the pupil the world 'looks' into us, if we accept such an anthropomorphic simile. By means of 'light waves' emanating from them, tree, table and cat penetrate into my eye, rather than my eye reaching out into the space where they are. The eye merely *receives* impressions – it is no magic lantern, projecting images, it releases no probing rays into space to perceive the cat's fur at the place where it is. The world delineates itself on my retina of its own accord, on the 100-odd million receptor cells crowded together there. Each one of them accepts a point of 'light', in other words, swallows a detail of the outside world, is aroused by this stimulus and conducts the stimulus in the form of an action current into the brain's dark depths, to the occipital lobes. In the optic nerve something like a million such pathways are crowded together.

The thing that has probably made comprehension of these mysteries more difficult than anything else, is the otherwise strikingly tempting comparison of the eye with a camera. A camera has a film at the back, or a frosted glass on which we can actually see the image upside down. The film, of course, might be compared with the retina – *but we do not see with the retina alone!* The eye itself is but a link in a much larger organ system, the whole of which is needed for visual perception. Every incoming image is subdivided into millions of stimuli that are transformed into action currents and conducted to the brain. It is there that I see a cat or a tree. Should the central brain parts be destroyed, I should be struck utterly blind, even if my external eyes remained intact. The brain as a whole comprises some 14 thousand million cells, and something like two or three thousand million take part in building up my picture of the room.

It is amazing enough that we can project the Grand Canyon on to a postcard. A photograph of the sun shows a structure within which 1,300,000 spheres the size of the earth could be accommodated. It is rather like that with our tiny eyes – what they reproduce of the great world finds room inside a small segment of the surface of a sphere. But these images, encoded in the action currents of the optic nerve, in no way resemble what we see on the frosted glass of a camera – any more than the electromagnetic waves flooding our television set from space resemble the voice of Aïda or King Lear's sorrowful countenance. It is the circuitry of the set and the brain that restores them to the 'original' image. In the one case that image is projected on the screen before us, while within ourselves it is reconstructed in the recesses of the brain. To say it once again, it is there that I see tree or animal. Whether I see them as they 'actually are' – that is one of the mysterious questions in the German philosopher Immanuel Kant's inspired *Critique of Pure Reason*.

When I approach the cat and touch it with my hand, I do not really see my hand 'out there,' any more than anything else. Similarly, I am aware of the sensation of touch only in my brain. Seeing is not a mere matter of receiving stimuli, but rather of becoming aware of them. Since that does not take place in the eyes alone, we cannot really say that it is the eyes that see and look out into the world. The implications are rather overwhelming. It follows that visual space, the entire objective space of the putative outside world, must be looked for *within me*, within the experiential space of the self. I am, so to speak, in a dark room, watching a sound-film, the physical elements of which are supplied by the auditory and optic nerves. There is no way out of this prison. I cannot force my way back through the nerves to reach true reality. Everything outside is conveyed to me through my senses. Yet my interior space is so overwhelmingly bright and organized with so many nuances that it is too weird and preposterous *not* to regard it as exterior space. I merely conclude that the clouds drift along the sky far away from me – the sky that I alone see is actually visible to me only in my brain bunker. Everything – room, table, cat, sky – comprises in the first place nerve currents, electromagnetic messages, codes flowing into the brain, before I see it. Just how the world itself really looks remains a closed book to me. I call the rose I see within me red, the sugar I taste within me sweet. Their inherent nature I cannot know. Just as everything King Midas touched turned to gold, so all existence I touch through my senses turns to a semblance within me.

Popular representations of brain function usually show us a back-to-front cross-section through the head, with the optic nerves forming electric conductors into a smoothly running telephone switchboard. Possibly there is a substation, where a technician develops the incoming 'film', sending it on by a pneumatic system to a secretary in the occipital lobe. The secretary examines the images and reports their content and meaning to the higher brain centres. Alas, peopling our thought circuitry with such secretaries explains nothing. We should have to posit another whole perceptive system in the secretary's brain, and so on *ad infinitum*. The perceiving self does not look once again with inner or possibly 'spiritual' eyes at the substance of the action currents flowing from the eyes into the brain. Just how it becomes aware of material substrata remains to this day an impenetrable mystery.

Idealists have long contended that dreams prove we experience the world only in our imagination. What happens to us in dreams is indeed strange enough. We lie asleep with eyes closed in a dark room in, say, mid-winter, dreaming most realistically that we are standing on a Mediterranean beach in bright summer sunshine. Ships pass by and dwindle in space, we hear the clatter of a helicopter in the air, yet beyond all doubt all this happens entirely within ourselves. We may even succeed in seeing ourselves in a mirror while dreaming; and yet exterior space and what we see of ourselves indubitably exist only in the interior space of ourselves. In dreams, memory provides the stimuli, but when we are awake, they come from the outside world, which seems to have an existence of its own, but which is an 'outside' we perceive solely in our 'inside'. Memory is always an unreliable fellow, likely to make things up, while by day we are under the tyranny of clear-cut exterior stimuli, determined by the laws of causality. When a cat moves, arises and arches its back, the stimuli depending on it change with the utmost precision; and in this way the rising and stretching creates an image within me. I see only the image of the cat. If some night we were to dream that we saw our room exactly as we know it when we are awake, our awakening self could merely confirm what we already saw in the dream: the dividing line between dream and reality would essentially vanish.

When the sun shines, we believe it is light outside, and the brightness remains, even when we shut our eyes, while a blind person cannot perceive it, precisely because of his blindness. Yet what actually floods the earth are merely electromagnetic waves, and we cannot possibly know whether they are indeed inherently 'light'. Light is of a certainty solely within me, where the stimuli from the waves that seem to have their own existence are transformed into brightness and luminosity. Light itself does not actually flow through the optic nerves, only a current that creates an awareness of brightness in the receptive consciousness. This world of light is overwhelmingly rich, and that is why it is so hard for us to know the totally different dream life of the blind, governed solely by senses other than sight. Dream events, in other words, illuminate the same space within us that is lighted in broad day. I am a visionary solely within myself, in my interior space, and it is there that I see the vastness of the Grand Canyon, the loftiness of the Alps, the abysmal distance of the stars. The world is indeed a semblance within me. I do not produce it on my own, however. It is a code, a symbolic image of a world that does have existence outside me. Inevitably, some thinkers succumbed to the proposition that there is no real world of things having an existence on their own, that it is only imagery, that our self merely creates subjectively the world we know so well. If this were so, we would be eating only imaginary apples and the world would indeed vanish completely when we disappear from the scene. Kant said it was scandalous that it was so hard to prove there is a real outside world. Like no other, he saw through the illusion; but he never disputed the *Ding an sich*, the thing in itself, merely all claims that it could be adequately 'cognized'.

Gottfried Keller, the Swiss poet, said that his eyes were his beloved windows on the world, and he hoped they would drink in its golden abundance as long as the lids were open. Actually, a window looks neither out nor in, it merely allows the electromagnetic waves to pass through the glass in either direction. Even that sounds far too anthropomorphic, as though the glass had some kind of control over it, when the passage is purely mechanical. The eye too is a window, through which electromagnetic waves pass in only one direction, triggering excitations that reach the brain. There they create an interior stage, with an illusion of space, or they light up the stage. When I see a primadonna on a real stage, I actually see her only on the stage reproduced within me. The real stage has a double existence – first in the outside world, and then within me, and I see only the one inside me.

Even when we speak of the brain as a 'dark room', we only add confusion. Beset by the problems of explication, we ever look for similes, and then give in to their blandishments, the moment they seem to be successful. When I flick the switch at night, the lamp lights up and the room grows bright. Actually, the brightness is entirely within me. Unless one heeds the lessons of epistemology, one will naturally assume that the lamp has illuminated a room that was dark before; but actually, the brightness is only inside me. It is in me that a light is kindled, while I believe automatically that the real room is being lighted, instead of merely the room of my mind. I myself cannot be described as 'lighted' – I merely sense an inner brightness; nor would we find the brain to be 'illuminated', if we could look inside it.

A blind friend of mine was fond of speaking of red roses, of bright days, which he thought he could perceive from the warmth of the sun; but when I put a white rose into his hand, he described it as red. When I visited him in the evening, he usually sat in total darkness, pulling on the stub of a cigar, drinking chianti and reading his beloved Shakespeare in braille. Of course I like to turn on the light, but when on one occasion I did not, without letting him know, he, of course, was unable to note that it was still dark.

He was also fond of telling me about his

sensations of light; but since he had been blind from childhood, I could only guess at what he meant. When I tried to describe brightness to him, he thought it partook of a fabulous character, something like a sharp and precise feeling of touch. He quite 'saw' the plausibility of Kant's teaching that light occurs only within us. Nevertheless, he could not grasp it, since his organs of sight were never stimulated, and without such stimulation he was unable to build up a picture of the visible world.

The world with all its dazzling and delightful qualities is a world we picture within ourselves. It is a phenomenon of consciousness, an event that occurs only in the imagining self. In his zeal of discovery, Kant bestowed less justice on the world existing outside than he did on the subjective sphere, which he enhanced as did no man before him. For even though the joys of a grand ball may be experienced only within ourselves, we should experience nothing, unless the senses were stimulated by the outside world. Kant overlooked the peculiar abundance that accrues to the senses. Man, in the act of cognition, does stand in a world that seems to have independent existence; but he himself belongs to that world and its existence. It is the existing world that becomes man. Consciousness and self are parts of the world. Can the world-become-man be so profoundly alienated from consciousness that it can no longer recognize itself in consciousness, as it really is? Here all the deep intuitions and intimations that perceive consciously our becoming aware of outside existence come back to the fore. The locus of that awareness is the self – the tiny human self in which the world-self becomes aware of itself. Why should sensation alienate existence from itself? Let such thoughts move your soul – and they will change your life. You will stand in awe not only of Nature's grandeur, of the mysterious stores of memory, as did St Augustine, but of the entire nature-grown self-organism with its magical power of imagery – the prefigured, elder, existing self rather than the limited, personal self that is linked with it. You may begin to understand that greater self at the bottom of you, thrusting from the depths of existence. That which we call a rose, by any other name is still a rose.

There was once a man who said 'God
Must think it exceedingly odd
  If he finds that this tree
  Continues to be
When there's no one about in the Quad.'

RONALD KNOX

Dear Sir, Your astonishment's odd:
I am always about in the Quad.
  And that's why the tree
  Will continue to be,
Since observed by Yours faithfully, God.

ANONYMOUS

9

Words and Pictures

The problem of word, object and image preoccupied the painter René Magritte all his life.
Here are his musings, dating back to 1929, about the pictures shown below:

1   No object is so tightly bound to its name that one could not give it another and better-fitting name.

2   There are objects that can do without a name.

3   An object impinges on its image, it impinges on its name. The image of an object impinges on its name.

4   Sometimes the name of an object stands for its image.

5   Some objects suggest the existence of other objects behind them.

6   Everything points to the conclusion that there is scarcely any relationship between an object and its representation.

7   In an image, words have the same force as shapes.

8   Indeterminable shapes may substitute for precise images.

9   No object has the same effect as its name or image.

10   Sometimes names in a picture designate definite objects, while images designate the indefinite – or sometimes the other way round.

11   Actually, a word may take the place of an object. A picture within a sentence may take the place of a word.

12   The visible contours of objects impinge on one another in reality, as though they formed a mosaic.

Words and Their Roots

Even educated linguists are often unaware of the roots of words in their mother tongue:
Hammock = *hamaca*, borrowed from the Arawak Indian culture; lily = from an Egyptian-Coptic word pronounced almost identically; cherry = Greek *kerásos*; carafe = from Arabic *garràfa*, via French; rose = Persian *wródon*, thorn-bush; tulip = from Turkish *tülbend*, turban; cinnamon = either from Hebrew *qinnāmōn*, or Malay *kayumanis*, sweet wood; blouse = ancient city of Pelusium, famed for making blue smocks; charlatan = Italian *ciarratano*, seller of indulgences; uncouth = originally 'unknown', from couth, old past participle of *cunnan*, to know; handicap = from hand in cap, an old game; jeopardy = from Latin *jocus partitus*, via French *jeu parti*, a drawn game; whisky = Scots-Gaelic *uisque-baugh*, water of life.

Wordplay

KIRSCH
CHRIESI
CERISE
CHERRY

Even simple words are subject to many different interpretations, may give rise to amusing confusion or can bring on hopeless contradictions. From the context of our visual memory, each word elicits images attuned to our particular personality. Whether we communicate or talk over one another's head may be a matter of chance association, of ingrained prejudice, of a lively imagination, all entailing a multitude of cerebal processes. And when it comes to such complex value-charged terms as freedom, justice, mind, soul, good, evil, communication becomes even more difficult!

Prejudice then takes over its baneful arbitrament, gives rise to an almost biblical confusion of tongues, sets mind against mind in bitter controversy: 'Alas! we live in an age in which it is easier to split the atom than to overcome prejudice.'

ALBERT EINSTEIN

An Honest Tale Speeds Best Being Plainly Told

SHAKESPEARE, RICHARD III, IV.iv

Since the Age of Humanism, especially, quotations from the Bible and the classics have been the stock in trade of the educated, who were ever intent on flinging them about to show their intellectual eminence. Having gained currency by much use, such winged words often served to convey the message the speaker could not formulate on his own. Maria von Ebner-Eschenbach, the German writer, said wryly that phrases had to go on foot for a long time, before they could take wing; but nowadays we are assailed on every side by modish sesquipedalian locutions used by pseudo-experts to lend authority to their dicta. Since such phrase-mongering has become a favourite pastime, let us here try to make a proper game of it, in aid of those whose supply of recondite terms needs refurbishing, in order to lend glamour to their trivia.

The illustration at the right needs little explanation. The column of figures and the three columns of words on page 13 are pasted on four rotating tobacco tins. All in all, the three word-tins are capable of providing **140,608 three-word combinations, which you may** use quite unblushingly, since none will dare admit he does not know what they mean. By way of practice, use the speech below, in which you simply fill the gaps with any random combination from the 'Gobbledygook Table' on the opposite page.

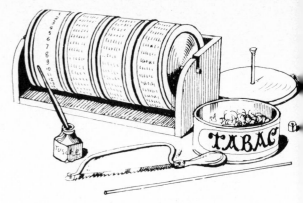

Ladies and Gentlemen!

I speak to you in the name of the Preparatory Commission, appointed in January 84 by the Conference for . . . . The Commission was given the mission of clarifying the question of . . . . I shall dispense with the preliminaries, since you all know the background, and come to the point immediately.

From the moment that press and television postulated the . . . , the insistent call for . . . has never ceased, rightly or wrongly. The fact is that none disputes the need for . . . . It is further true that neither . . . nor . . . have changed the situation in any way.

Your Preparatory Commission therefore immediately tackled the idea of . . . raised before, and subjected it to careful analysis. We concluded that the only new approach would be . . . , although we realized at the same time that one obstacle would be . . . which might indeed result in . . . . Fortunately, this unwelcome eventuality could be forestalled by means of . . . . Let the gentlemen who believe in . . . take note of this!

We should bear in mind that . . . and . . . are likely to favour our plan, and in the existing situation, we have no choice but to agree to . . . .

Ladies and gentlemen! the alarming increase in . . . challenges us to take far-sighted measures that are not without risk. There are, of course, possible alternatives, such as . . . and . . . , to say nothing of . . . which should not be under-estimated. We shall not know the chances of success, until, with the help of . . . and the deliberate use of . . . , we launch a pilot project. . . . might possibly bring an adverse reaction, but we must take that chance, for to resort to . . . would be to invite . . . confusing the public. Only time will tell whether we may then proceed to realize . . . and . . . , but much water will flow under the bridge before then.

This much is certain even today, ladies and gentlemen: In the long run . . . and . . . will not meet the needs of this generation. Whether these needs lie in the direction of . . . cannot be foreseen today. We are confident, however, that . . . and . . . will help us on our way.

I trust I have not presumed on your . . . ladies and gentlemen, and I thank you for having given me your attention.

Whate'er you think, good words,
I think, were best.

SHAKESPEARE, KING JOHN, IV. iii

Gobbledygook Table

1	Inherent	Coincidental	Interference
2	Emancipative	Exemplificatory	Efficiency
3	Substantial	Preventive	Interdependence
4	Ambivalent	Expansive	Projection
5	Reversible	Participatory	Motivation
6	Permanent	Degenerative	Eventuality
7	Gradual	Aggregating	Diffusion
8	Partial	Universal	Mobility
9	Societal	Falsificatory	Vacancy
10	Adequate	Evolutionary	Flexibility
11	Global	Appropriative	Finality
12	Responsive	Prior	Phase
13	Traditional	Illusory	Transparency
14	Dialectical	Concordant	Adaptation
15	Fictitious	Allocated	Factionalism
16	Defunctionalized	Frustrated	Extension
17	Existential	Restrictive	Periodicity
18	Positivistic	Accidental	Denudation
19	Elitist	Fluctuating	Affinity
20	Predicative	Simulated	Transcendence
21	Ultimative	Digital	Specification
22	Temporal	Convergent	Psychosis
23	Intransigent	Totemic	Competence
24	Obsolete	Elongating	Structure
25	Anti-authoritarian	Innovative	Disparity
26	Flanking	**Homogeneous**	Escalation
27	Multilateral	Identifying	Synthesis
28	Bilateral	Transfigurative	Consistency
29	Representative	Discrepant	Motivation
30	Quantitative	Culminating	Mobility
31	Concentrated	Diversifying	Cancellation
32	Ameliorating	Alliterative	Sufficiency
33	Divergent	Usurpative	Equivalence
34	Indicative	Erupting	Turbulence
35	Immanent	Deteriorative	Discontinuity
36	Synchronous	Obstructive	Potency
37	Contradictory	Decentralized	Expectancy
38	Differentiated	Imitative	Accumulation
39	Systematized	Co-operative	Plasticity
40	Inductive	Conglomerate	Stagflation
41	Structural	Progressive	Permanence
42	Integrated	Recessive	Epigenesis
43	Determinative	Programmed	Solidification
44	Coincidental	Eliminative	Application
45	Nonfragmenting	Differential	Implication
46	Interfractional	Complementary	Deterioration
47	Descriptive	Dynamic	Constructivism
48	Coherent	Substantive	Polarity
49	Fortuitous	Contributory	Classification
50	Proliferative	Component	Deformation
51	Compatible	Uniform	Extrapolation
52	Distributive	Exponential	Feasibility

Vaterland

The meaning of a word is inseparable from its typographical appearance. The form of the letters can emphasize a certain meaning, dramatize or negate it – and even make it seem absurd. Just try to insert the different scripts shown here into Cicero's famous saying: 'Wherever I flourish, there is my home.'

(German, *Vaterland*, literally fatherland.)

Vater- land !

Vater land

Variations on the word Vaterland. Exercises from the Hamburg Fine Arts Academy. Illustration at lower left from Bucher Studio, Lucerne, Switzerland.

The Subjective Reality of the Environment

The real world and the world we experience are two different things. We do not see an oak tree as it is. Every living creature extracts from it those parts that fit into its own personal world.

1   To the forester, the tree is part of the forest economy.

2   To the child, the tree is part of his magic world.

3   To the fox, the root hollows are home.

4   The owl enjoys the protection of the branches.

5   The bark provides nourishment for the ant.

6   The bark-boring beetle lives between bark and core.

What would our picture of the oak tree be, if in addition to the visual image, we had at our disposal sensual messages provided by paws, smell, claws, antennae, tactile bristles?

Diamond cut Diamond

Two cats   by Ewart Milne

One up a tree
One under the tree
The cat up a tree is he
The cat under the tree is she
The tree is wych elm, just incidentally.
He takes no notice of she, she takes no notice of he.
He stares at the woolly clouds passing, she stares at the tree.
There's been a lot written about cats, by Old Possum, Yeats, and Company,
But not Alfred de Musset or Lord Tennyson or Poe or anybody
Wrote about one cat under, and one cat up, a tree.
God knows why this should be left to me
Except I like cats as cats be
Especially one cat up
And one cat under
A wych elm
Tree.

Quand un Vicomte . . .

by Maurice Chevalier

Quand un vicomte
Rencontre un autre vicomte,
Qu'est-ce qu'ils se racontent?
Des histoires de vicomte!

Quand une marquise
Rencontre une autre marquise,
Qu'est-ce qu'elles se disent?
Des histoires de marquise!

Quand un cul-de-jatte
Rencontre un autre cul-de-jatte,
Qu'est-ce qu'ils débattent?
Des histoires de cul-de-jatte!

Chacun sur terre se fout, se fout,
Des petites misères de son voisin
D'en-dessous
Nos petites affaires à nous, à nous,
Nos petites affaires, c'est ce qu'ils
Pensent avant tout.

Malgré tout ce qu'on raconte,
Partout, partout
Qu'est-ce qui compte en fin de compte
Ce qui compte surtout c'est nous!

Quand une bigotte
Rencontre une autre bigotte,
Qu'est-ce qu'elles chuchottent?
Des histoires de bigotte!

Quand un gendarme
Rencontre un autre gendarme,
Qu'est-ce qui les charme?
Des histoires de gendarme!

Quand une vieille tante
Rencontre une autre vieille tante,
Qu'est-ce qu'elles exemptent?
Des histoires de frou-frou.

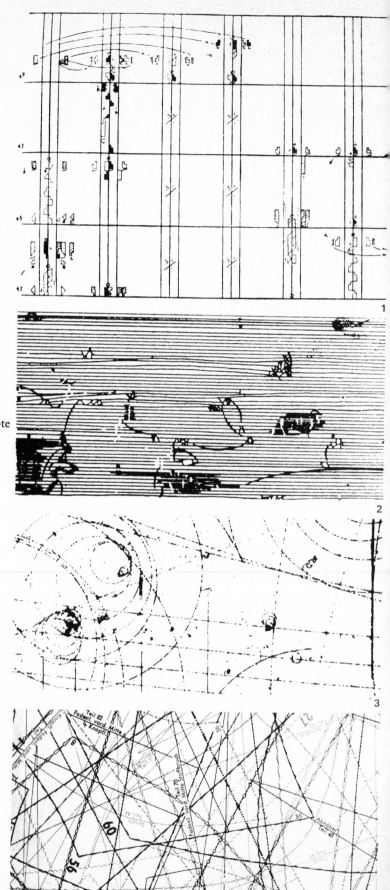

1   Orpheus attacked by the Furies,
choreography by George Balanchine.

2   Graphic notation of a piano
piece by Sylvano Bussotti.

3   Atomic particles in a bubble
chamber; in such chambers
physicists are able to trace the
pirouettes of the tiniest components
of matter.

4   Section from a dress pattern.

Babel on Every Hand

And the whole earth was of one language, and of one speech. / And it came to pass, as they journeyed from the east, that they found a plain in the land of Shinar; and they dwelt there. / And they said to one another, Go to, let us make bricks, and burn them thoroughly. And they had brick for stone, and slime had they for mortar. / And they said, Go to, let us build a city and a tower, whose top may reach unto heaven; and let us make us a name, lest we be scattered abroad upon the face of the whole earth. / And the Lord came down to see the city, which the children of men builded. / And the Lord said, Behold, the people is one, and they have all one language; and this they begin to do: and now nothing will be restrained from them, which they have imagined to do. / Go to, let us go down, and there confound their language, that they may not understand one another's speech. / So the Lord scattered them abroad from thence upon the face of all the earth: and they left off to build the city.

GENESIS 11:1–8

Just as every nation cultivates its own tongue, so every speciality has its own language. Experts in the field will instantly read and decipher the coded messages on the facing page. They see a train of movement, they hear music, they recognize the laws of physics, they trace the cut of a gown. Yet to the layman these messages convey no meaning, though they fascinate him, like symbols from another world. We are all of us initiates in a few fields and laymen in most others!

Konrad Lorenz, the famous Nobel-Prize-winning German student of animal behaviour, tells a charming animal anecdote, reproduced below in facsimile of his handwriting, complete with his own illustrations. It concerns the bus fares to be charged for various animals in Britain and Bavaria. The English lady, as we can make out, is willing to pay for her pet turtle, but the conductor advises her not only that 'squirrels in cages is birds', but that 'tortoises is hinsects, we won't charge you none for that'. His Bavarian colleague not only agrees on this point, but also that 'cats is dogs'. Whether or not his unwilling passenger was compelled to pay a fare is not made clear in the manuscript!

```
jollymerry
hollyberry
jollyberry
merryholly
happyjolly
jollyjelly
jellybelly
bellymerry
hollyheppy
jollyMolly
marryJerry
hoppyBarry
heppyJarry
boppyheppy
berryjorry
jorryjolly
moppyjelly
Mollyjelly
Jerryjolly
bellyboppy
jorryhoppy
hollymoppy
Barrymerry
Jarryhappy
happyboppy
boppyjolly
jollymerry
merrymerry
merrymerry
merryChris
ammerryasa
Chrismerry
asMERRYCHR
YSANTHEMUM
```

001

```
goodk kkkkk unjam ingwe nches lass? start again goodk
lassw enche sking start again kings tart! again sorry
goodk ingwe ncesl ooked outas thef? unmix asloo kedou
tonth effff rewri tenow goodk ingwe ncesl asloo kedou
tonth effff fffff unjam feast ofsai ntste venst efanc
utsai ntrew ritef easto fstep toeso rryan dsons orry!
start again good? yesgo odkin gwenc eslas looke dout?
doubt wrong track start again goodk ingwe ncesl asloo
kedou tonth efeas tofst ephph phphp hphph unjam phphp
repea tunja mhphp scrub carol hphph repea tscru bcaro
lstop subst itute track merry chris tmasa ndgoo dnewy
earin 1699? check digit banks orryi n1966 endme ssage
```

001

```
TEYZA PRQTP ZSNSX OSRMY VCFBO VJSDA
XSEVK JCSPV HSMCV RFBOP OZQDW EAOAD
TSRVY CFEZP OZFRV PTFEP FRXAE OFVVA
HFOPK DZYJR TYPPA PVYBT OAZYJ UAOAD
VEQBT DEQJZ WSZZP WSRWK UAEYU LYSRV
HYUAX BSRWP PIFQZ QOYNA KFDDQ PCYYV
BQRSD VQTSE TQEVK FTARX VSOSQ BYFRX
TQRXQ PVEFV LYZVP HSEPV TFBQP QHYYV
VYUSD TYVVY PVSZZ PCYJP FRDFV QYEVQ
PJQBT CYFES JQSZP QTTQZ DQRQZ VQUSP
TFRWP VCEYJ TZQSR JYEXP QOYFV XCYJP
MCYPV CQSWF AUSVP QTSRM GYYSX VQUSP
```

001

Everything You Can Do, I Can Do Better . . .

In the Middle Ages Rabbi Lev Ben Bezalel in Prague fashioned an artificial man of clay, the Golem. His modern reincarnation, the computer, can calculate anything in the world, even music, the dance, poetry, architecture, graphics.

001

The Golem was rendered animate by the written name of Jehovah, placed behind its forehead. Ultimately, when its maker tried to make it work on the sabbath, it killed him. What guiding formula is built into the computer's pseudo-brain?

011

010

100

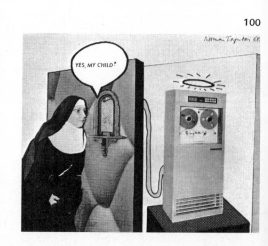

18

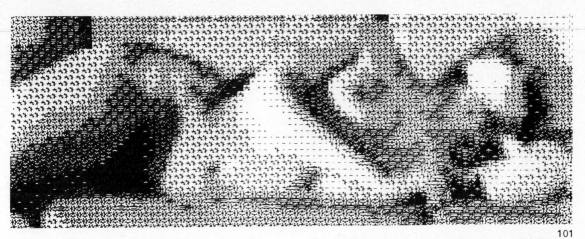

101

001 *Computer poetry: left and centre, Christmas cards; right, code poem.*

100 *Suggestion for a religious programme, by Norman Toynton.*

010 *Crossed diamonds computerized into images of President Kennedy and a dog.*

101 *4,000 manikins =1 nude.*

011 *Relief Transformation, by Efraim Arazi.*

110 *Op art experiment.*

110

1

A Dollar, if You Fall for It . . .

2

Discourse

Dr Seem and Dr Sense
Went to a café.
Seem believed in abstinence,
Sense, he ordered tea.

Talk and gossip was their scheme,
Food their recompense,
Specious meringue ordered Seem
Scottish egg did Sense.

Each sought the other to regale,
Their talk was glib and smooth,
Each tried to tell the taller tale
And each one stretched the truth.

Seem talked nonsense to friend Sense –
Sense, it seemed to Seem,
Answered only with pretence,
Bits taken from a dream.

The evening hour arrived anon,
Neither of them spoke.
Seem faded when the lights came on,
Sense went up in smoke.

Adapted by Heinz Norden
from Zwiegespräch *by F. Hardekopf*

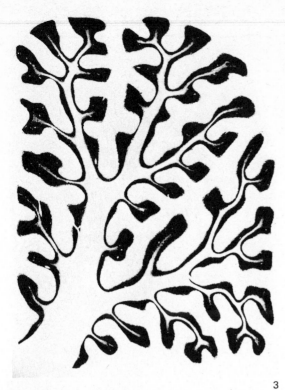

3

4

Nature and Art

Abstract art related to nature? Well, is there any reason why an artist, in his slow process of maturation, should not end up with forms and structures that are linked to natural law? They are, after all, part and parcel of the world, and how can he evade them? The artist serves as a kind of creative microscope. Leonardo da Vinci advised artists to contemplate ancient walls, the grain of wood and other natural structures. Every generation, whether in science or art, finds its creative fulfilment in its own way.

1 Supermarket, Medina, Illinois; or pop art by Paul Bianchini, New York?
2 Pubic shield in carved Wengé wood, Mgamo tribe, Niefeld Collection; or abdominal plate of a trapdoor spider, Cyclocosmia truncata, *Florida?*
3 Cells of the cortex of the human cerebellum. Microphotograph by Professor R. Schenk, University of Basle, Switzerland.
4 Collage by Henri Matisse, 1947.
5 Microphotograph of copper oxide.
6 Painting by Pablo Palazuelo, 1955.

5

6

The Relativity of Magnitude

Patterns of memory are formed within us only by exposure to things. By vision and touch, the brain gains a design of the external world – even in the absence of any proof that it is actually like our idea of it. In his 1952 painting *Personal Values* (above), Magritte juxtaposed a number of familiar objects that are incongruous because of their disproportionate size. Children usually dwell in a world in which known and familiar objects are much more important than those they do not recognize. Indeed, they tend to ignore the unfamiliar or at least to consider it un-important. Adults often forget that children have to grow into our world of established forms and values, by continuing experience. For us, the world stays the same size, but children, in the course of time, see those frighteningly huge grown-ups, animals and objects shrink to 'normal' dimensions. We do not fully understand that for a two-year-old a window-sill is 'overhead', chairs offer an exercise in mountain-eering, the space under a table can be a cosy room and the living-room itself is about the size of what to us would seem a gymnasium.

We adults would face a similar problem, were we translated to an unfamiliar world, with objects not adapted to us in size and purpose. We would be in the position of Lemuel Gulliver shipwrecked in a land of giants, where everything is ten times the familiar size at home. Almost powerless as he is, he is compelled to endure frightful encounters with giant rats and flies. He is revolted by the overwhelming physical presence of the giants. 'This made me reflect upon the fair Skins of our English Ladies, who appear so beautiful to us, only because they are of our own Size, and their Defects not to be seen but through a magnifying Glass, where we find by Experiment that the smoothest and whitest Skins look rough and coarse, and ill coloured.'

Journey to Brobdingnag

by Jonathan Swift

'I remember when I was at Lilliput, the Complexions of those diminutive People appeared to me the fairest in the World; And talking upon this subject with a Person of Learning there, who was an intimate Friend of mine; he said, that my Face appeared much fairer and smoother when he looked on me from the Ground, than it did upon a nearer View when I took him up in my Hand, and brought him close; which he confessed was at first a very shocking Sight. He said he could discover great Holes in my Skin; that the Stumps of my Beard were ten Times stronger than the Bristles of a Boar; and my Complexion made up of several Colours altogether disagreeable: Although I must beg Leave to say for myself, that I am as fair as most of my Sex and Country, and very little Sunburnt by all my Travels. On the other Side, discoursing of the Ladies in that Emperor's Court, he used to tell me, one had Freckles, another too wide a Mouth, a third too large a Nose; nothing of which I was able to distinguish. I confess this Reflection was obvious enough; which, however, I could not forbear, lest the Reader might think those vast Creatures were actually deformed: For I must do them Justice to say they are a comely Race of People.'

Room with furniture twice the normal size, from an exhibition in Zürich.

Gulliver in Brobdingnag and Lilliput.

The Effect of Contrast

Large and small, light and dark are qualities we can evaluate only in their reciprocal relations. We judge on the basis of contrast. Considerable influence is wielded by the environment.

A circle standing alone remains undefined in magnitude. Add a human hand and it will take on shape and size of a ball. Add a gondola and suggest a landscape, and it becomes a balloon dozens of feet in diameter.

Smaller units close by have a magnifying effect. The cathedral in the picture opposite – it happens to be the one in Gdansk – owes its powerful effect to the propinquity of small dwelling-houses en masse, surviving from

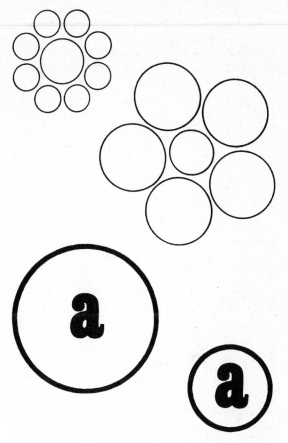

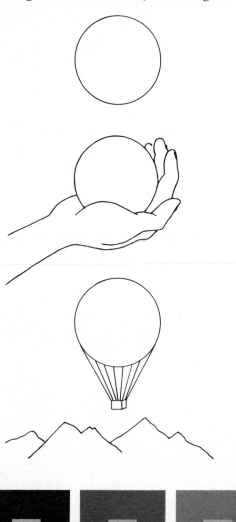

centuries past; but when skyscrapers come crowding in on an old city, they dwarf even a mighty cathedral, as seen in the picture of St Patrick's, New York, at lower left on the opposite page, and the artist's rendering of what Brussels is planned to look like in the future, lower right.

Give a figure enough room, and it will appear relatively small; but when you fence it in closely, it seems almost to burst its frame. The central circles in the two assemblages at the top are the same size, and so are the two letters 'a'.

The inner squares in the six large ones below all have the same tint. They appear different only because of the changing background. A colour test makes this even plainer. A red field will seem more and more luminous as red is withdrawn from its background, reaching a peak when the background is green.

The Moon Illusion

Three of these four copies of Samuel Palmer's picture *Coming from Evening Church* have been retouched. Which one shows the moon at its actual size?

The panel at upper left. The panel at lower left is as the artist painted it, showing his subjective impression of the size of the moon.

When near the horizon, the moon is unconsciously compared with the outlines of houses and hills at the skyline and perceived as much larger than it actually is – up to thirty times! The sun, huge and distant, and the moon, much smaller but relatively near, are seen as discs of the same size, less than half a degree across. The area of each is only about the one-hundred-thousandth part of the visible sky, and both seem relatively small in size when they stand high in the sky, where they cannot be compared with a familiar terrestrial object.

Within our angle of vision or in a photograph taken with a camera with standard lenses, the moon disc pre-empts 1/25 to 1/35 of the picture width, as shown in the picture of the Parkes radio telescope in New South Wales, Australia, on the opposite page.

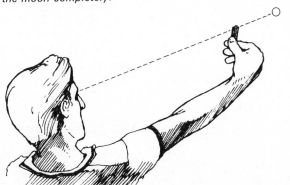

Three matchsticks, held at arm's length, obscure the moon completely.

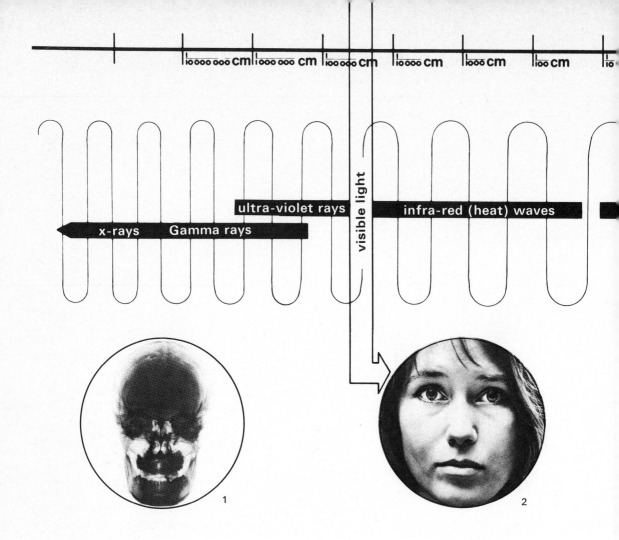

x-rays   Gamma rays

ultra-violet rays

visible light

infra-red (heat) waves

1

2

The Window of Visible Light

When one stops wondering at the wonderful, it stops being wonderful.

CHINESE PROVERB

This is how Hermann von Helmholtz, the physiologist, described the deficiencies of the human eye: 'If an optical instrument maker tried to sell me an instrument that possessed the defects of the human eye, I should, without exaggeration, feel fully justified in criticizing his slovenly work in the harshest terms and virtually flinging his product back at him.' Yet we take the greatest delight in that part of the world that is visible to us – visible in colour, a capacity we share only with the primates. Much of the energy emitted by the sun is in the form of light. No wonder the

living creatures of our earth have developed ever better eyes to perceive it, from vague distinction of light and dark to that of black and white, with sharp contours, and ultimately the ability to sense the colours of the spectrum with their thousands of nuances. Colour is an essential element of all things for us. We can explain the origins of colour and marvel at it, but we cannot form a real picture of it. What happens is that energy input shifts electrons from the inner orbits of atoms to ones that are further away. When they leap back to their old orbits and surrender the energy they have absorbed, light results. A return from the fourth ring of electrons to the third, for example, gives rise to red light. When the leap is from the fourth to the second, the result is blue light. Our vision of the mysterious colour dance of these tiny atomic particles turns our reality into a curtain before a magic stage. To perceive the surface magic of colour and form, the human eye had to specialize on an extremely narrow band in the almost infinite range of waves. A difference of only a few ten-thousandths of a millimetre in wavelength spells the difference between visibility and invisibility. The

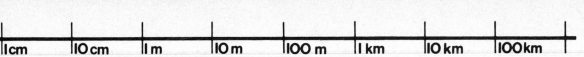

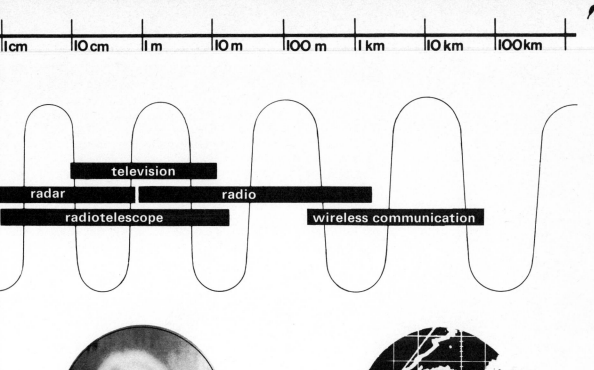

television

radar · radio

radiotelescope · wireless communication

3

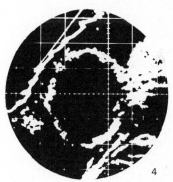

4

wavelength of red light is 0.00007 cm, that of violet 0.00004. The 'imperfection' of our visual organ allows us to recognize but the outer fragments of our environment (Fig. 2). Actually, the universe vibrates with an immense volume of electromagnetic radiation. If we could receive the whole range of it, the result would be chaos and confusion. It would be like listening to a radio set that received all stations simultaneously. Even if the visual receptors in our eyes were able to distinguish radiation into the range of long waves and short waves, the brain's storage capacity would ultimately fall short of being able to decipher it all. Still, conceivably other environmental criteria might have, in the course of natural selection, resulted in an eye attuned to a different wave-range. In that event, our picture of the world would be radically different. Our systems of ethics and aesthetics might be focused in different ways. For an x-ray eye (Fig. 1), body-building and luscious curves would have little meaning, while a well-healed fracture of the clavicle might be a titillating sight that would have to be concealed, in puritanical cultures, with a finely worked metal shield! A heat eye would

reach into the infra-red range and be especially sensitive to thermal radiation. A white winter landscape would be a frosty black to the infra-red eye, while an unlighted dairy stable would shine in many nuances of warmth. Fig. 3, an infra-red picture, is a male portrait in thermography. A long-wave eye would, so to speak, serve as an 'acoustic eye', able to turn sound into image, as doctors do with their ultrasonic devices that enable them to observe the growing foetus in the womb (Fig. 4). Painters of the long-wave world could make their compositions visible by means of an orchestra, but pneumatic drills, motor-cycles and other noisy machines would be ruled out, for fear of 'blinding' the audience. Politicians might stand a better chance of success, since their voices might make up for much of their lack of 'vision'. The surface picture, which is all we can see of our environment, remains full of mystery, and the wealth of its things far transcends our vision. Eyes, ears and the sense of touch and taste send many messages from which we build up a kind of mosaic, but many pieces are missing, and we cannot locate them, because we lack sense organs receptive to them.

About Seeing

The retina is the farthest outpost of the brain; the apparently simple act of seeing is a complex mixture of perception, recognition and thought which is learned only through long practice and exposure to appearances. Many illusions arise when too much importance is accorded to the interpretative stage: it is easy to be tricked by the brain into seeing what we expect, not what is there (below left).

The objects of our environment are registered in two different retinal images, inverted top to bottom and left to right (below right). The left half of each image is transmitted to the right visual cortex of the occipital lobe, the right half to the left visual cortex – the visual receptors having first translated the images into the language of electrical impulses which the brain can read. To the child, the world is still topsy-turvy; only the experience of touch slowly teaches the brain how to rethink its images. This is a mysterious process which is not yet fully understood. But there is a fairly popular experiment which shows that each eye can actually perceive a separate image: as we consume more and more alcohol, the ocular muscles of convergence grow paralysed and we tend to 'see double'.

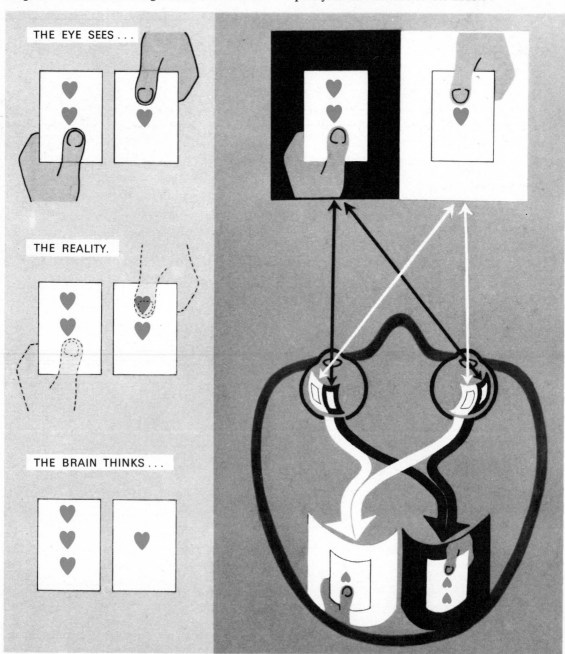

THE EYE SEES...

THE REALITY.

THE BRAIN THINKS...

The world is mirrored in our eyes much as it is on the surface of these silvery globes. Leonardo thought that since we see the world upright, light rays must cross not only in the pupil, but once again in the vitreous body of the eyeball. It was Johannes Kepler, the German astronomer, who realized that our visual apparatus is so constructed that it can produce only inverted images, while Helmholtz concluded that we learn to see only by adjusting vision to touch, so that we ultimately ignore the inversion and see everything 'naturally'. G. M. Stratton, the British psychologist,

Here is a simple way of demonstrating that images on the retina are actually inverted. Prick a hole in a card and hold the opening against a bright background. Then hold the pin, head up, close to one eye (the other being closed). Within the bright disc of the pinhole the pinhead, although held upright, will appear head down, showing that the eye works much like the lens of a camera.

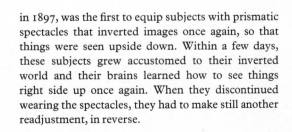

in 1897, was the first to equip subjects with prismatic spectacles that inverted images once again, so that things were seen upside down. Within a few days, these subjects grew accustomed to their inverted world and their brains learned how to see things right side up once again. When they discontinued wearing the spectacles, they had to make still another readjustment, in reverse.

Seeing by Halftone

One hundred and twenty million sensitive receptors in the retina carve up the image into point-sized messages, not unlike the technical approach of the Pointillist painter Signac (picture below) or the halftone process of reproducing pictures (picture above). The light messages are collected by a vast number of nerve fibres that leave the eye as the optic nerve. Every second, millions of mini-messages race along these nerve pathways into the brain's dark-room, where several billion cells have a share in interpreting the images, which are perceived in a scale of tonal values. To gain an impression of the original picture instead of seeing just the dots of varying intensity resulting from the halftone screen through which it was photographed, regard the upper part of this page from the far end of the room.

Displacements

by Tim Head, 1975: installation at the Rowan Gallery, London

Photographic images taken in a gallery, then projected back as slide transparencies on to the gallery walls, incorporate various apparently casually placed objects. A directional shift from the areas originally photographed to their present projected location sets off a chain reaction of displacements – images of a chair and a bucket of water tilt precariously over their real counterparts, a ladder's image extended across floor and wall is set alongside the actual object flat up against the wall.

Illusion and reality are superimposed upon one another in such a way that, despite the clarity of the 'devices' employed, the discrepancies between them can never satisfactorily be resolved.

The Impossible Fact by Christian Morgenstern

Palmstroem, old, an aimless rover,
Walking in the wrong direction
At a busy intersection
Is run over.

'How,' he says, his life restoring
And with pluck his death ignoring,
'Can an accident like this
'Ever happen? What's amiss?

'Did the state administration
'Fail in motor transportation?
'Did police ignore the need
'For reducing driving speed?

'Isn't there a prohibition
'Barring motorized transmission
'Of the living to the dead?
'Was the driver right who sped . . .?'

Tightly swathed in dampened tissues
He explores the legal issues,
And it soon is clear as air:
Cars were not permitted there!

And he comes to the conclusion:
His mishap was an illusion,
For, he reasons pointedly,
That which *must* not, *can* not be.

Translated by Max Knight

33

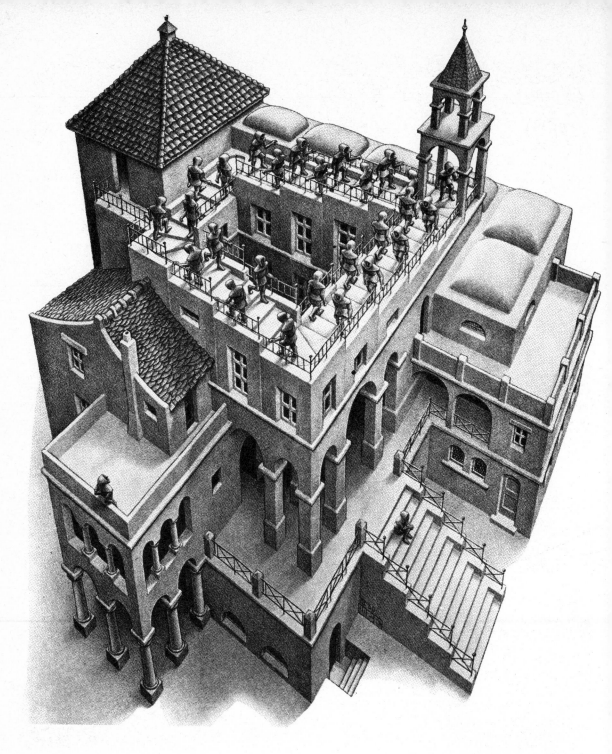

Upstairs, Downstairs
A 1960 lithograph by M. C. Escher

An oblong courtyard is enclosed by a building roofed with a continuous stairway. The denizens seem to be monks, members of some unknown order. Their ritual duties apparently include walking this stairway for several hours each day. When they grow tired of ascending it, they may descend. Both directions seem to be meaningful but actually lead nowhere.

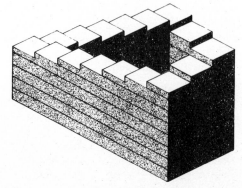

Waterfall
A 1961 lithograph by M. C. Escher

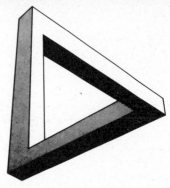

When we follow the details of this construction with our eyes, we seem unable to discern a single flaw. Yet as a whole it is impossible, because of the occurrence of sudden changes in interpreting the distance between our eyes and the object. In the Escher picture this impossible triangle (right) is used three times. Falling water spins a millwheel and then flows 'down' through a flume in zigzag fashion between two towers until it reaches the point where the waterfall begins anew. The two towers are of equal height, yet the right one is one storey lower than the left.

Above left: This withered leaf is actually the pupa of the Cruiser butterfly, from Malaysia.

Above: The Swallow-tail moth larva feeds only at night; during the day it rests, disguised as an ordinary twig.

Above: An example of somatolysis in two Puss moth caterpillars.

Right: When disturbed, the Mexican Bull's-eye moth shows these false 'eye spots' to scare off predators.

The Outlandish World of Mimicry

by Walter Linsenmaier

Insects display almost unlimited skill in the art of camouflage, eliciting our astonishment, admiration and curiosity, as well as a desire to study how and why they practise it. They blend into their background and resting-place, be it soil or rock, foliage or bark – but that is only the first phase of insect mimicry. Actually, they project optical illusions that seem even more purposeful.

There is, for example, the kind of mimicry called somatolysis, in which conspicuous markings transect the insect body at rest, seemingly dividing it into unrelated parts. It is found especially among forest dwellers, where it is aided by the rapidly shifting interplay of light and shade. Other insects choose the opposite strategy, underlining their corporality but imitating lifeless objects – odd bits of dry or rotting wood, fresh or dry and twisted twigs, thorns, smooth or wrinkled seeds and nuts, tatters of lichen; or again, many kinds of different leaves, green, withered, dry, rotting, with or without a stem, lying on the ground or dangling from a

Some insects live in permanent colonies, while others group only to rest, forming plausible 'inflorescences', like these cicadas.

tree or shrub, sometimes deliberately waving as though in the wind, or realistically 'moth-eaten'. These replicas may even show mildewed spots or silvery dewdrops or what looks like bird droppings or fallen petals. Insects that form colonies when at rest may take on the shape of clusters of blossoms.

What makes this fascinating variety even more striking is the complex coincidence of colour and line, shape and attitude, and even the choice of locale, whether the perpetrators of this mimicry are butterflies or moths, beetles or bugs, grasshoppers or cicadas. One and all, they behave as though they had practised before a mirror. They 'rest' in positions that seem all but impossible. Thorax or abdomen may be abducted at a steep angle, or other body parts may be stuck out stiffly into the air; and harmonizing with these theatrical skills may be imaginatively coiffed or trimmed bristles, or aggregations of scales, all to the end of blurring the true body contours and rendering the illusion well nigh perfect.

Insect nature, however, has even further optical means for preserving its kind, namely the contrary effects of drawing

attention, warning and frightening. In some instances, when the camouflage is penetrated and the supposed leaf or bit of wood recognized as something edible, the insect may

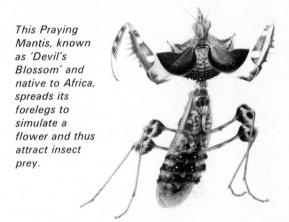

This Praying Mantis, known as 'Devil's Blossom' and native to Africa, spreads its forelegs to simulate a flower and thus attract insect prey.

suddenly display a garish colour. The underlying idea is to startle and often enough the trick succeeds. Enough time is gained to make good an escape, perhaps only to a near-by shrub, where the creature once again may assume the pose of an innocent supernumerary leaf. Often the eyes have deterrent markings, such as bright white highlights, or rings of black, blue, red or yellow, that can be brought into view, or a bright red abdomen may be suddenly brandished.

Warning colours, by the way, are displayed permanently by insects that are well armed, noisome or poisonous and therefore have no need of camouflage, but on the contrary seem virtually to wish to call attention to their power, rather after the manner of the luridly coloured coral snake. These militants, however, often have 'fellow travellers' that use bluff in place of the power they lack, imitating the conspicuous appearance of the invulnerable models, for which they would like to be mistaken. Thus harmless flies may

Larva of a domestic bug that camouflages itself with dust and particles of soil.

more or less closely resemble poisonous spiders or stinging wasps.

The insect world is full of such remarkable survival mechanisms, many of which have but recently become known. How many more are there, so successful that we may never 'blow their cover'?

Left: Flowering rocks.
Mesembryanthemum
pseudotruncatellum, *native
to South Africa, is one of the
most remarkable members of
the succulent family, if not
the whole plant kingdom, on
account of its striking
resemblance to a pebble.
Only when it flowers does it
look anything like a plant.
Careful observers should be
able to pick out at least
twenty-seven individuals
in this picture.*

Right: Picture of pictures in a
picture. This assemblage is
not a collage, but a
meticulously executed
trompe-l'oeil *painting by the
eighteenth-century artist
Michele Bracci.*

The Chameleon

The name of this remarkable reptile means 'ground lion' in Greek. Its ability to change its colour to match its environment is another example of nature's genius in harnessing deception to survival.

The peppered moth (opposite page), *Biston betularia*, has pepper-and-salt wings that marvellously adapt it to its birch-bark habitat, affording it protection from predatory birds. Chance mutation created a black variety that multiplied in Britain's soot-blackened industrial regions, where its dark coloration provided better camouflage and therefore an improved chance of survival. Recent 'clean air' policies in Britain have actually resulted in this moth turning perceptibly lighter again!

Few military installations can boast of cam-ouflage to match that of certain animals, to which mimicry gives protection against their enemies. Is this astonishing phenomenon a matter of mere chance, a game played by nature? Or was Jean-Baptiste Lamarck, the French naturalist, right when he said – this was about 1800 – that an inventive spirit was ultimately responsible? And why were all the other hungry animals foolish enough to let themselves be deceived over aeons of time? Nature, in the course of time, simply gave rise to a multiplicity of variants, most of which succumbed to the vicissitudes of life, while for a very few a minute departure from the character of their kind gave improved adaptation for survival, as compared with their ancestors. They won out in the struggle for

Two peppered moths, Biston betularia, *resting on a lichen-covered trunk. The lower moth blends in with its surroundings; its darker, more conspicuous companion is an example of the melanic form which has evolved in industrial areas.*

food, light and living-space. The arts of deception they developed enabled them to maintain their species over the ages.

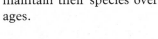
Mutt and the snake.

Miss Wagner's Glass Eye

from *Roughing It* by Mark Twain

You see, Sile Hawkins was – no, it warn't Sile Hawkins, after all – it was a galoot by the name of Filkins – I disremember his first name; but he *was* a stump – come into pra'r meeting drunk one night, hooraying for Nixon, becuz he thought it was a primary; and old deacon Ferguson up and scooted him through the window and he lit on old Miss Jefferson's head, poor old filly. She was a good soul – had a glass eye and used to lend it to old Miss Wagner, that hadn't any, to receive company in; it warn't big enough, and when Miss Wagner warn't noticing it, it would get twisted around in the socket, and look up, maybe, or out to one side, and every which way. . . . Grown people didn't mind it, but it most always made the children cry, it was so sort of scary. She tried packing it in raw cotton, but it wouldn't work, somehow – the cotton would get loose and stick out and look so kind of awful that the children couldn't stand it no way. She was always dropping it out, and turning up her old deadlight on the company empty, and making them oncomfortable, becuz *she* never could tell when it hopped out, being blind on that side, you see. So somebody would have to hunch her and say, 'Your game eye has fetched loose, Miss Wagner dear' – and then all of them would have to sit and wait till she jammed it in again – wrong side before, as a general thing, and green as a bird's egg, being a bashful cretur and easy set back before company. . . . Old Miss Wagner was considerable on the borrow, she was. When she had a quilting or Dorcas S'iety at her house she gen'ally borrowed Miss Higgins's wooden leg to stump around on; it was considerable shorter than her other pin, but much *she* minded that. She said she couldn't abide crutches when she had company, becuz they were so slow; said when she had company and things had to be done, she wanted to get up and hump herself. She was as bald as a jug, and so she used to borrow Miss Jacops's wig. . . .

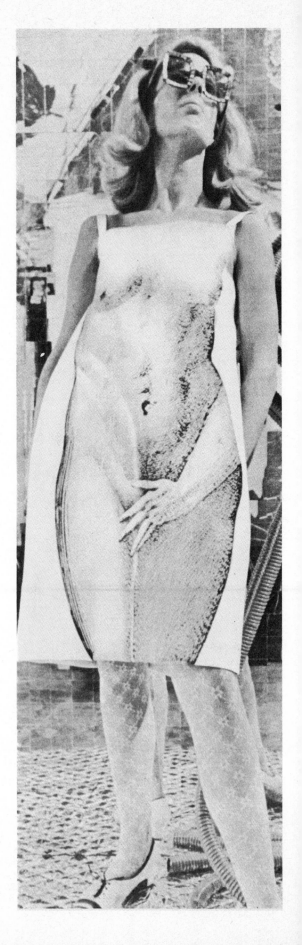

Clothes Make the Man (or Woman)

This American paper dress of 1965, imprinted with Botticelli's Aphrodite, exemplifies a typical fashion trick: concealment, as conventionally prescribed – but concealment that actually stimulates, by drawing attention to and emphasizing what is supposed to be concealed, often in such a way as to promise more than the 'naked facts' can fulfil.

Women's dress – or sometimes undress – focuses on many 'charms', but men really have but one asset to boast about in the game of sex. The Renaissance put up no fewer than thirty-six criteria of beauty in a woman, while men had to rest content with one, their codpiece, often brightly coloured and padded to implausible dimensions, as shown in the engraving of a medieval mercenary at lower left and the various forms of sixteenth-century penile armour with which often ageing and rheumatic field captains paraded their virility. Penis braggadocio goes back to primitive times, as shown in the picture of a member of the Dani tribe at lower right. Not content to display his testicles freely, he exaggerates the size of his member by means of a huge scabbard.

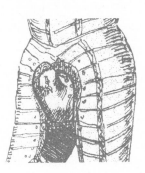
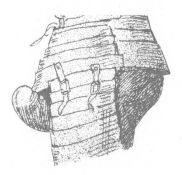
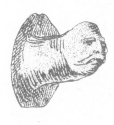

Trick Packaging

from Homer's *Odyssey*

'Demodocus, I praise thee far above all mortal men, whether it be the Muse, the daughter of Zeus, that taught thee, or even Apollo, for right duly dost thou chant the faring of the Achaeans, even all that they wrought and suffered, and all their travail, as if, methinks, thou hadst been present, or heard the tale from another. Come now, change thy strain, and sing of the fashioning of the horse of wood, which Epeius made by the aid of Athene, even the guileful thing, that goodly Odysseus led up into the citadel, when he had laden it with the men who had wasted Ilios. If thou wilt indeed rehearse me this aright, so will I be thy witness among all men, how the god of his grace hath given thee the gift of wondrous song.'

So spake he, and the minstrel, being stirred by the god, began and showed forth his minstrelsy. He took up the tale where it tells how the Argives of the one part set fire to their huts, and went aboard their decked ships and sailed away, while those others, the fellowship of renowned Odysseus, were now seated in the assembly-place of the Trojans, all hidden in the horse, for the Trojans themselves had dragged him to the citadel. So the horse stood there, while seated all around him the people spake many things confusedly and three ways their counsel looked; either to cleave the hollow timber with the pitiless spear, or to drag it to the brow of the hill, and hurl it from

the rocks, or to leave it as a mighty offering to appease the gods. And on this wise it was to be at the last. For the doom was on them to perish when their city should have closed upon the great horse of wood, wherein sat all the bravest of the Argives, bearing to the Trojans death and destiny. And he sang of how the sons of the Achaeans poured forth from the horse, and left the hollow lair, and sacked the burg. And he sang of how and where each man wasted the town, and of Odysseus, how he went like Ares to the house of Deiphobus with godlike Menelaus. It was there, he said, that Odysseus adventured the most grievous battle, and in the end prevailed, by the grace of great-hearted Athene.

Translated by S. H. Butcher and Andrew Lang

Hello, darling, are you coming over for your Easter egg hunt? (R. Peynet)

More about Packaging

by Harald Scheerer

Illusion, wherever you look – clothes, wigs, make-up, gestures, boxes, bottles, book-bindings, labels, walls, envelopes . . . one might continue indefinitely. Every package, every shell, every surface tells less than the truth underneath.

Take packaging proper: it may be changed to suit changing circumstance; and as the situation changes, so does the illusion. Packers had their own guild as early as the Middle Ages, a sign of the importance even our forefathers assigned to the exterior of things.

Or take the matter of weight: some packages make the content look heavier than it actually is. This is an increasing source of irritation to the public and the authorities.

Or packaging used deliberately to deceive: goods may be offered at a price below the (misleading) one printed on the package.

Or packaging used to make the cheap seem dear and the dear cheap: elaborate packaging may make shoddy merchandise seem valuable or expensive contents seem like a bargain.

Or take women: do they not really deserve charter membership in the Packers' Guild? Have you ever observed a girl who has set her cap at a man interested only in a wife possessed of all the domestic virtues? You may be sure she will dress (or 'package' herself) conventionally and conservatively, to project an image of domesticity, whether she possesses these virtues or not. Or take a girl seeking to appeal to a man known to prefer sophistication. You may be sure she will find the precise 'package' for her campaign.

Or take the matter of marketing – an example: a major wine merchant needed labels for his five different clarets. His advertising agency wished to test the effectiveness of five labels it had designed, covering a wide range of colour, typography and illustration. The five labels were pasted on five bottles, each of which contained exactly the same claret. The only difference, in other words, was the label. A number of self-proclaimed wine experts were then invited to a tasting session. They agreed on the following descriptions for the five bottles:

No. 1: Light and agreeable.
No. 2: Heavy, high alcohol content.
No. 3: Very dry.
No. 4: Too sweet.
No. 5: Flat and insipid.

Each label, by its design and appearance, had projected a different illusion.

Put a bar of chocolate in a soap wrapping and to one not in the know it will taste of soap. Put a person's favourite brand of cigarettes in the pack of a rival brand and he is likely to say that it does not taste the same. Packages have a powerful influence on what is inside, or at least on how it is perceived and valued. This is as true of people as it is of goods, and in most cases the packaging is deliberately used to project an illusion.

Illusion is not necessarily the equivalent of deception. Most people find illusions pleasant and actively pursue them. There are, of course, the spoilsports who insist that the packaging does not matter, only the content. Yet, since 'anticipation is the better part of enjoyment' there are people who hate to open a beautiful package, lest the content disappoint them!

Take the cover of this book, which sets out to project the illusion that the content is interesting, readable and worth the purchase price. Is that not what made you buy it? Let us hope you found the illusion to be reality!

The Bathtub Sofa

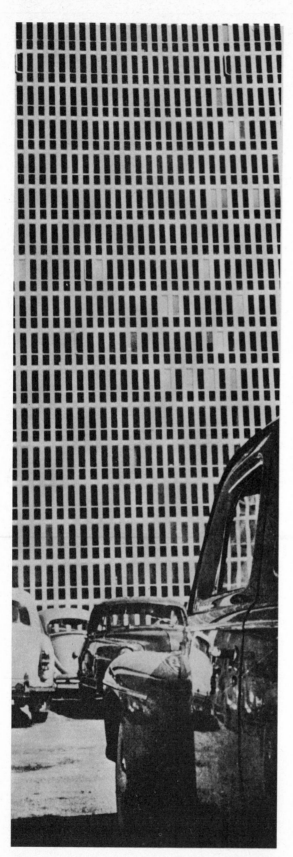

It is a fallacy to believe that anything can properly serve more than one purpose. The inventor Kastner in Paris tried to pervert a chandelier into serving as an organ and to turn an organ into a lighting fixture – but neither really worked. Nor did the combination sofa–bathtub–coffee table catch on at the turn of the century.

Left: Interchangeable modern architecture. Is this (a) the Sole Mio Tower apartments in Milan; (b) the UNESCO Library in Paris; (c) Elektra Co. headquarters in Zürich; (d) the Barbican, London Wall; (e) a multi-storey garage in Hamburg; (f) the Bristol Hotel in Los Angeles?

Art and Architecture: Things Are Not Always What They Seem

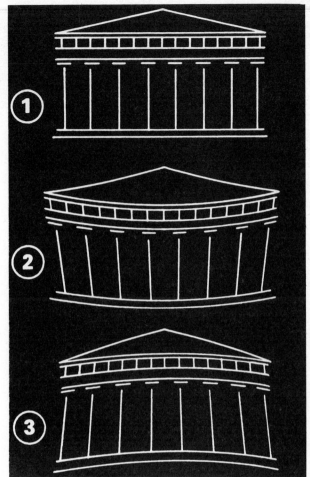

①

②

③

A case of optical correction: these sketches of the eastern façade of the Parthenon demonstrate the subtle means employed by its architects to enhance the visual effect.

1 The Greek temple as it appears to the beholder. All lines seem to run perfectly vertically or horizontally, although they are in fact concave or convex, as shown in Fig. 3.

2 If the building had actually been constructed in verticals and horizontals, as it appears in Fig. 1, it would look like this.

3 Actually, the Parthenon was built along the lines here indicated. The columns are tilted inward almost imperceptibly, while base, steps, architrave and pediment are curved upward slightly.

Constantin Brancusi, Endless Column, *1937.*

. . . The optical performance of the *Endless Column* is stunning, the elements do not *appear* to diminish. What happens is that as the sculpture moves upward, away from the eye, the proportions of each element progressively become more squat, the breadth increasing proportionately to the height; the relative proportion of the lowest full element is 2:1, height to breadth, of the highest full element, possibly 1:1. Of course there has been an *absolute* perspective contraction; but the optical law is subverted by the created optical fact.

WILLIAM TUCKER

Puzzle Pictures

Above: Trick landscape, by Martin Will.

Left: Virgin and Child in the Clouds, *by Rembrandt. Where is the angel?*

Below: St Helena. Where is Napoleon hiding?

Where is the old woman?

Where is the bridegroom?

Where is the farmer?

Where is the angler?

Dance of the Marionettes

by René Simmen

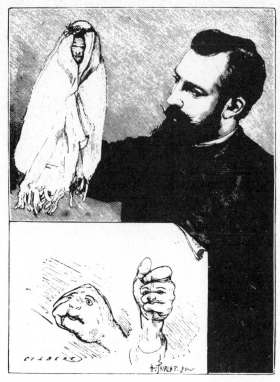

The hand puppet.

The fascination that emanates from a well-performed puppet play is hard to explain, for both puppeteer and public. On stage the puppet seems to awaken to a life of its own. Incomprehensibly, the puppeteer seems to bow to the puppet's wishes. As Max Bührmann put it, 'the initiative seems to pass to the puppets, and the puppeteer seems to have no choice but to obey them'.

As for the audience, it sees the puppet as an autonomous figure. The strings by which the marionettes are manipulated, the rods of the Javanese shadow figures, even the black-clad puppet animators in the Japanese Bunraku play – they all become completely invisible.

Not that this illusion is the result of realism in the execution of the puppet. Rather it stems from its abstract quality. Marionette-makers over-emphasize salient characteristics. Hands and heads are usually about one-third larger than in human proportions. Hair gives way to fur, wool or string. Glass eyes are often foregone and supplanted by shiny buttons or nail-heads, which are better reflectors of light and thus seem more 'human'.

Oddly enough, the jerky, mechanical movements of puppets serve to enhance the sense of reality. No human leading lady can give such eloquent expression to love as can the articulated wooden doll. No matinée idol can toss his head as imperiously or bow as humbly as a Chinese shadow player.

In the Romantic Age voices were heard advocating that all human actors should give way to puppets, and one wonders whether this idea was really so far-fetched. In Asia, at least, the puppet theatre has been able to gain a position of preferment, indeed, in one instance it actually became the model for a type of human theatre: the Japanese Kabuki players gained acceptance by adopting style and appearance of Bunraku puppets.

Puppet players are undoubtedly aware of the spell their puppets are able to cast over the audience; but the power the puppets manage

The earliest documentation of hand puppets in a manuscript of 1344.

Dance of the Korean maiden with her grandfather.

to gain over their manipulators is a phenomenon quite different from the emancipation of the puppets themselves. The medicine men in tribal cultures have always been aware of the power of moving effigies of their gods. However much the Church may hold aloof, the faithful flock to Madonnas that give the blessing and Saviours who bleed.

Perhaps puppeteers become the creatures of their puppets, when they identify with their players and make their roles their own. In Indonesia, the Dalang, manipulator in the shadow play called Wayang-kulit, achieves this identification by lapsing into a kind of trance. 'He speaks, screams, sings,' says Jacques Brunet, 'and increasingly succumbs to the spell of his figures. Soon this identification becomes complete, and it is no longer the Dalang who is speaking, but the actor figure that avails itself of him.'

This change is communicated to the audience – but not when the performance is broadcast by television. Then it seems clumsy and laboured. We conclude that the illusion is not just optical but stems from a mysterious rapport between puppeteers and spectators.

Shadow Magic

Modern media have displaced the shadow play, like many other dramatic forms of charm, profundity and old tradition. Only the children's game of casting shadow shapes on the wall manages to recreate some of the fascination, to give a hint of how shadows can create the illusion of three-dimensionality.

The origin of shadow plays must be sought in the Orient, in India. It was in Java, however, that the art developed its most highly stylized figures. Thence it travelled by way of Bali, Thailand and China to Iran and Turkey. Alert story-tellers of the Mediterranean, especially the Moroccans, popularized it and created many variant forms. In the seventeenth century, the *ombres chinoises* were brought to France, from where, in the following century, they reached America as *ombres parisiennes*.

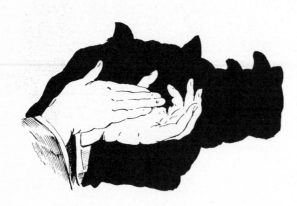

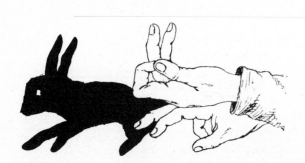

The World in Distortion

1

The arts of presenting plays, pageants, spectacles, triumphal processions and the like reached a high level in the sixteenth and seventeenth centuries, and many ingenious devices were employed, among them the curious forms of distortion called anamorphosis, in which apparently meaningless designs became recognizable when viewed in cylindrical mirrors or at extreme angles. Anamorphosis apparently goes back to Leonardo da Vinci. One of his 'abstract' scribbles in the collection of drawings known as the *Codex Atlanticus* consists of eight lines which, when the eye is held almost against the paper just beyond the left edge, turn into a child's face (Fig. 1).

The two sixteenth-century puzzle pictures by Ehard Schön on the facing page (Figs 3, 4) seem at first glance to be ordinary representations, but when viewed edge-on with the page held up to the eye, they reveal ribald scenes. Their conventional parts shrivel up into next to nothing, while the parts that make little sense when viewed head-on come into focus.

The meaning of the Greek roots of the word anamorphosis is 'transformation', and the term thus proves to be aptly chosen. A common everyday example is the word STOP (or other simple directions), painted on roadways at intersections in narrow letters many feet long, almost incomprehensible to pedestrian passers-by, but readily legible to the approaching motorist.

The photograph (Fig. 2) shows the kind of distortion that can be created photographically with a so-called 'fish-eye' lens.

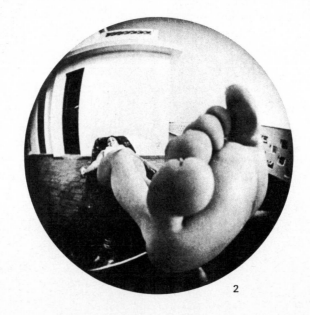

2

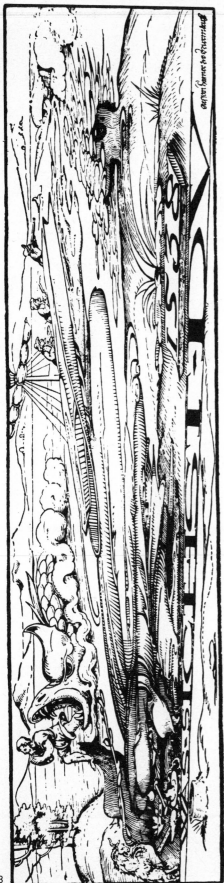

3

4

Anamorphous Pictures

Hans Holbein's 1533 painting *The Ambassadors* depicts Jean de Dinteville and Bishop Georges de Selves (Fig. 4, facing page). In this picture he seems to have given a premonitory hint of the ambassador's impending death at the Court

of St James's, by means of a mysterious oblique figure at the bottom which, viewed at an acute angle, is strikingly revealed as a skull. On reproductions of this painting, one occasionally finds that a zealous retoucher has obliterated the 'stain' and filled in the floor design!

Playful trickery of this type is no longer popular today, and even the once common distorting mirrors in amusement arcades and at shop entrances (Fig. 2) are disappearing. The cylindrical mirror (Fig. 5), which reconstructs a figure from the meaningless squiggles on the base, used to be a familiar sight at fairs and sideshows, but is today found but rarely in science museums.

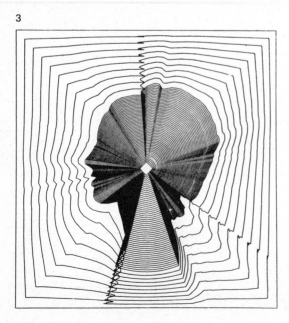

4

The seventeenth-century German scholar Athanasius Kircher was already designing these devices, which he dubbed *Magia anamorphotica*. In a way, they are the ancestors of today's computer programmes that can

create distorted representations (Fig. 3) on command. The two illustrations at the top of the facing page show an anamorphous portrait of Edward VI dating back to 1546, both head-on and from an angle.

5

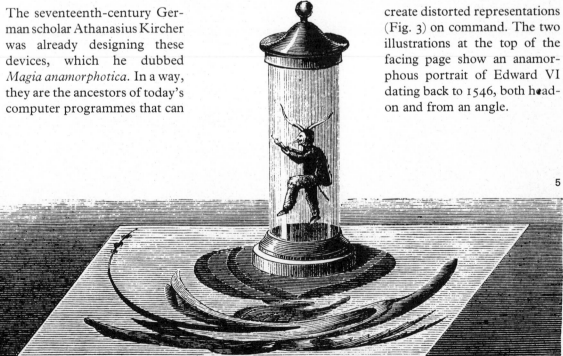

Mirages

In certain conditions of light and temperature, and of locations such as sea and desert, we sometimes see things that are not there, notably (looking along long stretches of highway, for example) bodies of water. The usual reason is that light reaches our eyes by two paths, because layers of air of different temperature have different refractive powers. A special kind of mirage, often seen in the Straits of Messina, is called 'Fata Morgana', which is Italian for Morgan le Fay, King Arthur's fairy sister (yes, the Arthurian legend has its Mediterranean variants!). Sometimes ships, oases and even whole cities are seen in the sky, inverted, right side up, or both (Fig. 2). We rightly speak of 'the clear mountain air', and it is true that people from smog-ridden cities commonly remark on the crystalline clarity of the Alpine landscape, where every tiny detail seems to stand out in the unpolluted atmosphere. A blanket of snow, however, tends to rob us of our standards of reference and we often under- or over-estimate distances, sizes and proportions. With the sun low in our back, giant shadows may be cast on a fog bank – or at least they seem huge to us, because the fog bank may be much closer than we think. This is the explanation of the famous 'Spectre of the Brocken' seen in the Harz Mountains of Germany (Fig. 1).

Since water is denser than air, it has a different refractive index (Fig. 6). A spoon in a glass of water may show a sharp bend, and our leg

1

looks crooked as we step into the bathtub. Whenever we move from one refracting medium to another, we must adapt our seeing, like divers or astronauts on the moon. Otherwise shapes and distances will deceive us.

How misleading reflections can be we see when we try to outline the image of our head on a fogged mirror. It turns out to be absurdly small – until we appreciate that it is twice as

2

3

far away as we think. In the case of the pictures of the Palazzo Vecchio in Florence (Fig. 4) and of the shopkeeper in his doorway (Fig. 5), we have trouble establishing our point of view. The facing mirrors (Fig. 3) exemplify geometric progression. Each time the picture of one of the two boys is reduced by one-half, into infinity. In theory, it can never disappear altogether.

4

5

6

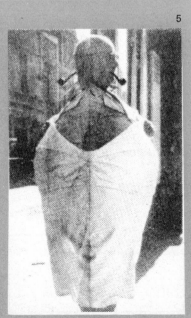

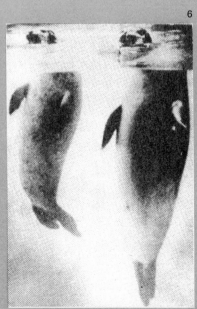

The Blind Spot

You Can't Have Your Cake and Eat It Too

Or, to put it another way, you can't have everything. Our eye, for example, does not actually see the entire visual field. There is always a 'hole' somewhere in the middle, because there are no visual receptors over an area about 1/16 of an inch in diameter, the optic disc or papilla or 'white spot' where the optic nerve and blood vessels enter the retina. A foot away, a postage stamp may vanish completely, at 12 feet a person's head, and at 65 feet we have no direct perception of an area one hundred times the size of the full moon's disc.

This astonishing hole in the visual field was discovered only comparatively recently. It was in 1668 that the physicist Mariotte created a sensation at the English court, when he demonstrated the blind spot by making ministers appear to be 'headless'. We can perform a similar experiment, using the pictures of the coin and the roll in the black strip above. Cover your right eye and look at the coin. When your eye is about 16 inches away, the roll will vanish. The band will look black throughout – and if it were a different colour, it would look that colour throughout. It is your brain that fills the hole – it has learned to do that with whatever is seen around the hole. Our eyes are always moving, thus supplying the brain with a wealth of information about the whole visual field and enabling it to 'paper over', so to speak, the area that may not be actually seen at the moment.

Irradiation

Few optical illusions stem from garbled messages sent by the eye to the brain. 'Our senses do not deceive us,' said Immanuel Kant. 'This is not because they always judge correctly, but because they do not judge at all.'

Bright figures seem larger than dim ones. The dazzling disc of the sun, for example, appears larger than the moon that reflects its light at far lower intensity. Actually, both measure about half a degree of arc. Whenever a strong light stimulus is projected on the retina, it arouses not merely the receptors struck directly, but also those adjacent, since these cells are grouped into batteries. Proportionately more cells take part in reporting a lighted area than a shaded one of equal size.

When we see a bright figure against a dark background, some of the receptors in the adjacent dark region of the retina are also stimulated, beyond the actual contours of the bright image.

A honeycomb of white discs (lower right) almost blocks out the black interstices, when viewed from a distance or with unfocused eyes. This irradiation effect is one reason why dark sculptures that are to stand against light backgrounds are often made over life size.

In the Hermann grid illusion, we see the white bands whiter than they actually are, while grey spots appear at the intersections. The reason may be that the white at the intersections has less 'competition' from the black, less black to irradiate, hence looks less bright than the streets and avenues.

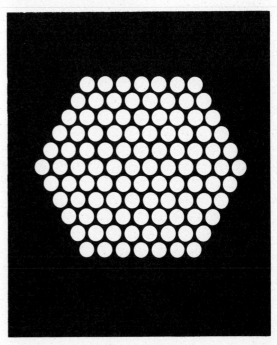

Blurred Vision

The cornea of the eye often has a slighter horizontal than vertical curvature which makes it impossible to see horizontal and vertical lines in a given plane in focus at the same time. When we allow our eyes to dwell on any of the three figures below, our vision of some segments of the circular lines will probably be indistinct. When we rotate the page in small circles, these lines are successively scanned by corneal quadrants of differing curvature, appearing focused and blurred in turn. As a result, the discs seem to spin. Now tear out transparent page TR-1 at the end of the book and arrange the upper circles beside the book as you rotate it. You will note that these fixed circles appear to spin exactly in phase with those you are rotating.

At birth, the eye is 'short' in comparison with its adult dimensions, and images projected through cornea, aqueous humour and crystalline lens come to a focus *behind* the retina. The eye, in other words, is long-sighted. In the process of growth, the globe lengthens and images slowly move up to the retina, for normal vision. If the front-to-back diameter of the eyeball becomes 'long' – as it does in about one-sixth of the population – images are focused *in front of* the retina and the eye becomes short-sighted.

Accommodation

Three groups of fibre alter the curvature of the crystalline lens, regulating the eye's focal depth. Accommodation enables a child to keep a point in focus at a distance from the eye of only two or three

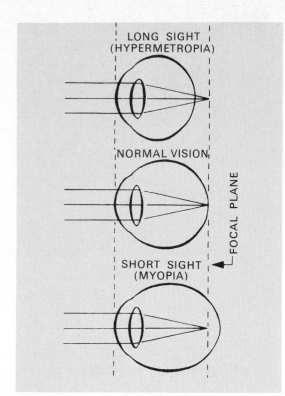

inches; but with increasing age, the lens loses elasticity. A normal-sighted person of thirty cannot bring his eyes closer than about four inches and keep the scale at the left margin in focus. At forty, the distance has lengthened to six inches, five years later to eight. At seventy, the lens has become almost rigid. The eye is 'presbyopic', which is the Greek for 'age-sighted'.

After-images

After-images are a sign that our visual receptors have become fatigued from seeing too much of the same colour. They occur when we stare unwaveringly at an object or figure for a fairly long period of time. When we look in a good light for ten to twenty seconds at the mouth in the face of the woman below left, and then shift to the corresponding spot in the black-and-white version at the right, our eyes

'recover' by seeing the background in the complementary colour, blue, while, by contrast, the face 'blushes' prettily. After-images become particularly intriguing when the picture or background to which we shift our eyes is itself of various colours.

Look at the central cross in the white-on-black picture at left centre in a strong light for about half a minute, and then shift to the cross in the white field at right centre, and you will instantly recognize the portrait in the after-image.

We cannot see what is directly in front of our nose, unless we squint. The picture of the bridge, below,

proves it. Bring the white gap in the middle closer and closer to your nose, and it will close.

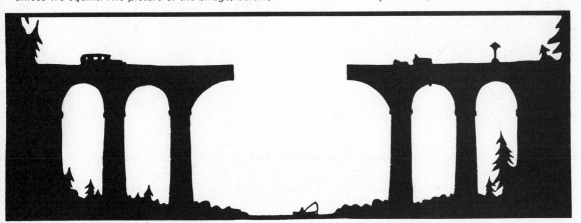

These three figures
from a collection by
N. Snearl are among
the most impressive of
all geometric optical
illusions. Over the past
few years they have
been credited to a
number of artists, but
their actual originator is
the British psychologist
J. Frazer, who
examined such figures
in a comprehensive
study published in the
British Journal of
Psychology in 1908
under the title 'A New
Visual Illusion of
Direction'.

Concentric Circles

We can convince ourselves that these figures are not spirals, ellipses or television-screen shapes, but rather perfect circles, when we trace them with a pair of compasses. A particular feature of these illusions is that no amount of reasoning and proof destroys the first impression, no matter how long and intensively we look at them.

It seems impossible to decide what share in this mis-interpretation is borne by the eye, and what share by the brain. One cause lies in the manner in which the circles are represented. The lines are alternatingly black and white rather than continuous, and they have black and white triangles attached to them.

Few people are aware that, oddly enough, our eyes are never entirely still. Even when we fix them on a point with a great effort of will, they are subject to a tiny involuntary 'flutter'. Now the brain's interpretation of an image projected on the retina is strongly influenced by the activity of the three pairs of muscles that move each eye. The circular segments in these figures tend to guide the eye inward toward the centre or outward toward the margins, and these diversionary manoeuvres are apparently seen in the brain as inherent properties of the images. Thus the concentric circles are 're-viewed' as irregular configurations.

The Magic of Motion

Only the patient camera, rather than our eyes, can appreciate the beauty and regularity of complex pendulum movements, because it is able to record them from beginning to end (see figures at right). When the eye sees twenty to twenty-five successive still pictures per second, an illusion of continuous movement is created. Riffle the pages of this book from back to front, beginning with page 71, and you will see horse and rider at the top corner trot off the page. The temporal resolving power of eye and brain is limited. As the speed of movement increases, lights turn into luminous bands, as happens with the swung torches in the picture above. We see a long jump only as a whole, unable to perceive the delicately balanced elegance of limb and muscle (see below). Unless they are lighted, objects moving near us at high speed become virtually invisible. We cannot see a bullet in flight.

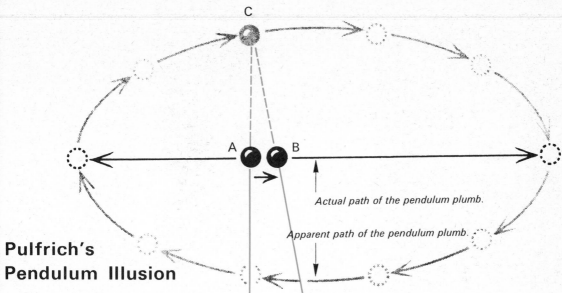

C

A B

Actual path of the pendulum plumb.

Apparent path of the pendulum plumb.

Pulfrich's Pendulum Illusion

If both your eyes are serviceable, you will be readily able to conduct the following experiment – the odd thing is that its discoverer was actually blind in one eye! Take a thin cord about four or five feet long, fix a weight to one end – a ping-pong ball will do very well – and allow this pendulum to swing at some distance in a plane at right-angles to the direction of your sight. Now when you cover one of your eyes with a filter of some kind, say one lens from a pair of sunglasses, or an exposed photographic film, the pendulum will appear to be swinging in an ellipse rather than a flat plane. If you light the swinging ball very strongly and keep it against a dark background, it may even seem to be describing something very close to a circle. The brain evidently gains this impression from being fed two retinal images of different intensity. A screened eye does indeed transmit its messages with a slight delay behind its unscreened partner. When the pendulum is at B, the right eye reports this to the brain normally, but the left eye is a bit late and reports the pendulum as being at A. Knowing that there is only one ball, the brain does not quite know what to do with the two different images in space, except to fuse them stereoscopically, which places the single image apparently at C, creating an illusion of depth where actually none exists.

With the help of a cardboard disc rotated by twisted double strings attached to each side, two separate pictures on the recto and verso can be readily made to coincide – Polly is seen inside the cage, the djinn in the bottle, etc. Or you can carefully cut a picture into a kind of two-part mosaic, taking even greater care in pasting the two parts (one of them upside down) in proper register on the two sides of the disc. When you then spin it, they will seem to blend once again.

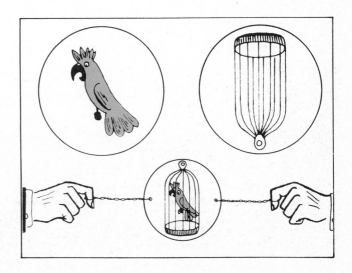

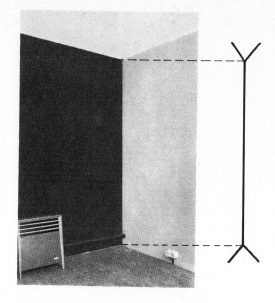

The Naked Eye

Listen to the French philosopher René Descartes speaking, in 1637, of the size constancy of objects, in his *Dioptrique*: 'Our judgment of form plainly derives from our knowledge or belief concerning the relative positions of the various objects concerned. These judgments seldom coincide with the images in our eyes, for those images contain ellipses and oblongs when we actually see circles and squares.' The three-storey building edge, above, and the room corner at upper right are the same height, as are the adjacent marker lines with arrowheads. Yet when the sides recede from the observer, the edge seems shorter than when they come toward him. The brim of the top hat, A–B at right, looks much smaller than its height, C–D. Yet both are exactly the same size. Horizontal lines seem shorter to us, because the eye movements required to take them in are easier to execute than up-and-down movements. Asked to draw a square with a side of about eight inches or larger freehand, most people will produce something that is 1/30–1/40 wider than it should be.

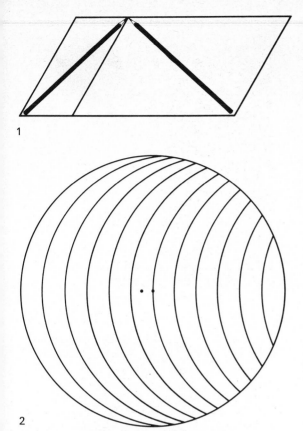

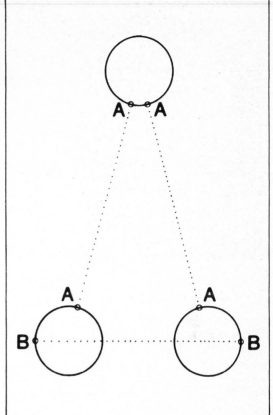

1

2

3

Fig. 1: The geometrical background with its two areas of unequal size induces us to misjudge the length of the two diagonal pencils, which is the same.

Fig. 2: The arcs inserted into the circle seem to push its centre towards the left. The true centre is shown to the right.

Fig. 3: The dotted lines A–A and B–B are of the same length. The way in which the circles are grouped makes it impossible to judge secondary relationships with even approximate accuracy.

Fig. 4: Our common impression of printed characters is that they are in proper balance. In some instances we feel that top and bottom are symmetrical, but when we turn them upside down, as in the two lower lines at right, we are surprised to note that, without our being aware of it, the lower part is actually larger than the upper.

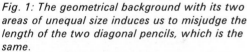

4

Fooling the Skin

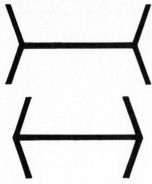

Fig. 1: The Müller-Lyer illusion is among the most thoroughly investigated, since it dates back to the noted early nineteenth-century German physiologist Johannes Müller. Just why the two horizontal bars persist in appearing to be of different size, however, even after the observer has verified that they are not, has not been unequivocally clarified to this day.

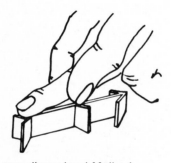

Fig. 2: As in the two-dimensional Müller-Lyer figure, the fingers are deceived into feeling that the line with the arrowheads 'going away' is longer than the one between the 'inward-pointing' arrowheads – although they are exactly the same length. This haptic illusion was discussed by Ann Watson and C. French of Aberdeen University in Nature, 26 February 1966.

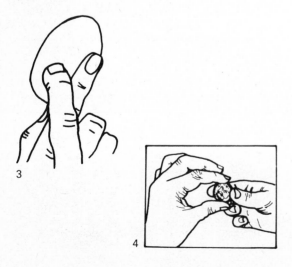

Almost everyone has heard about optical illusions, but it is much less well known that the sense of touch may also be deceived, especially when it is deprived of the aid of vision. A staple 'ordeal' of juvenile initiation ceremonies, for example, is to compel the candidate in utter darkness to plunge his hand into a vessel of slimy, clammy, wriggling worms, which is often followed by a fit of fainting or vomiting. When the light is turned on, the 'worms' are seen to be nothing more than a bowl of chilled spaghetti. Of course suggestion plays a part in this prank.

One of the most familiar optical illusions is induced by the so-called Müller-Lyer figure. The illusion mentioned on p.66 is precisely duplicated when the figure is executed in three dimensions and explored by the fingers, and it persists even in full vision – not unnaturally, since the eyes are themselves fooled by the two-dimensional version! Such tactile phenomena are sometimes called 'haptic illusions', from the Greek verb *haptesthai*, to touch.

Two other haptic illusions are here described and illustrated.

Fig. 3: When the tips of crossed index and middle fingers are lightly rubbed over a curved surface like an egg or a billiard ball, or for that matter the tip of the nose, one gets a strong impression that either two separate objects are being touched, or else one with a bumpy, lumpy surface. The reason is that the normal 'outsides' of the fingertips have become the 'insides'. The skin in touch is 'not used to' serving in that configuration and keeps signalling to the brain that something 'on the other side' is being touched, which is interpreted as being two distinct and discontinuous curved surfaces, or at best two separate 'bumps' on the same surface.

Fig. 4: Hold a large coin or a poker chip between left thumb and forefinger, and rotate it with the right thumb and forefinger, reaching around underneath with the forefinger and pushing with the thumb. Almost certainly you will get the persuasive tactile impression that the coin is oval rather than round. The horizontal axis will feel a bit longer than the vertical axis between the left fingers. The larger the disc and the faster it is turned, the stronger the illusion. Both of these illusions work best with the eyes closed.

Fig. 3: 'Aristotle's Illusion', as it is called (indicating how long it has been known!), is readily tested on one's own nose, or even another finger. The impression that one is touching two noses or fingers is quite strong.

Fig. 4: The 'Coin-Turning Illusion' was first described by Robert Cormack of New Mexico Institute of Mining and Technology in Science in 1973. The illusion that the object – any disc larger than one inch in diameter will do – is wider than it is high can become very convincing.

The Two Parallels

by Christian Morgenstern, translated by Heinz Norden

Two parallel lines went walking
Out into infinite space,
Two upright souls, not talking,
Well-bred and full of grace.

To sidestep intersection
Unto their blessed grave,
Such was their firm election,
For they were proud and brave.

Ten long light-years they wandered
And trudged on side by side,

Until at last they pondered
The sense of their lonely stride.

They had no way of knowing –
Were they still a parallel pair?
Like two souls they kept flowing
Through the eternal glare.

The infinite light overpowered them,
They blended as in a dream.
Eternity devoured them,
Joined like two seraphim.

All the lines of this extraordinary 'Temple of Wisdom' are straight and parallel.

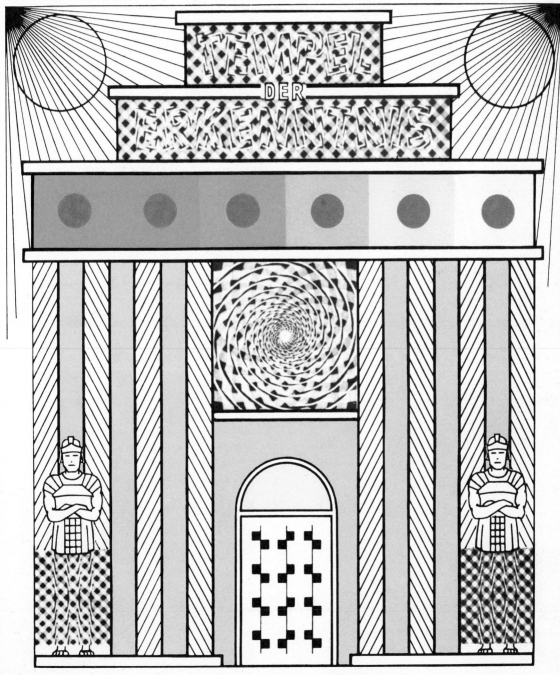

1

2

3

6

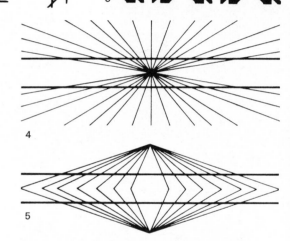

4

5

the lines begin to look more and more discontinuous as the angle of intersection grows more acute.

Supposed continuations of intersecting diagonals can be accurately verified only with the help of a ruler (Fig. 7). If you wish to check this, place the transparent tear-out page TR2 (Supplement) on this page.

Experiments with Lines

Zöllner, Lipps, Hering and Poggendorff are the names of scientists who studied these optical illusions. The parallel lines in Figs 1–5 are distorted by the secondary elements in the design. When walking past a colonnade of Gothic arches (Fig. 6), we may reach points from which the forward columns overlap the farther row in such a way that the pointed arches no longer seem to close symmetrically. The overlapping contours lead the eye astray. When a pattern of black stripes is placed so as to intersect one or more lines (Fig. 8),

7

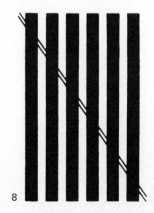

8

Pity the Poor Square!

Despite the fact that some of them look crooked, paunchy or dented, all the heavy squares below are of the same size and strictly straight and rectangular. In nature, eye and brain are never confronted with such extraordinary geometrical situations, hence they have no experience of how to reconcile and evaluate two clear-cut patterns in conjunction. The properties of 'figure' and 'background' cannot be sharply separated. The background pattern provides a kind of backdrop, as does the scenery for a stage play.

Try distorting the square at the right by means of a vigorous geometrical pattern of your own choice, e.g. various patterns of parallels. You can play this game, using other figures as well, with the help of the transparent page TR4 and also p. A1, both in the Supplement at the end (or beginning) of this book.

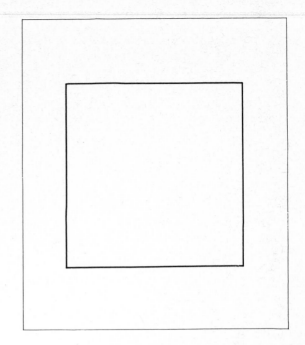

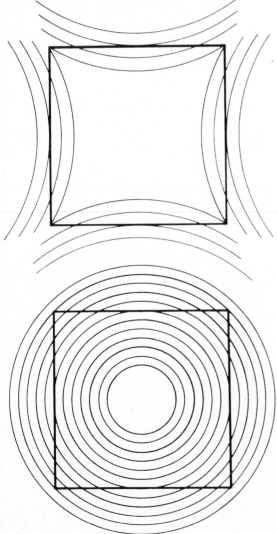

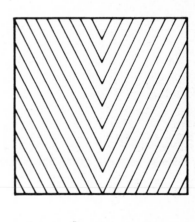

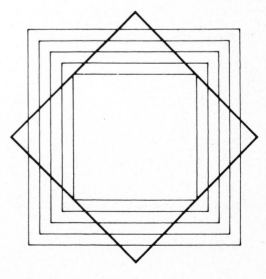

Hidden Patterns

One of the most fascinating illusions is obtained when we place two close patterns of lines one over the other. We are then no longer able to recognize the two patterns separately,

because their interpenetration gives rise – or so it appears to our eyes – to a secondary pattern of totally new dimensions. Colour printers become painfully aware of this, for unless they keep the half-tone screens of the separate colour plates carefully in register, the printed colour picture may display a splendid 'plaid' pattern. Such patterns are called *moiré*, originally a French term for so-called 'watered' or 'flamed' fabrics. One way of producing them is

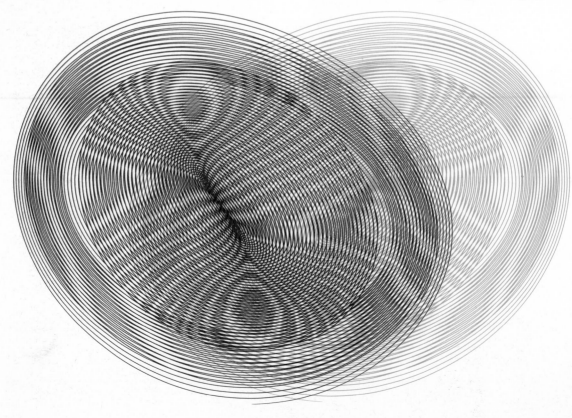

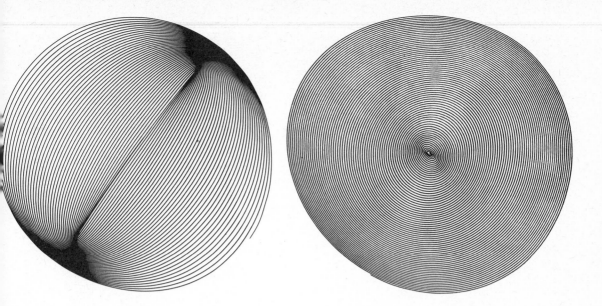

to press two sheets of fine silk between hot rollers. The warps and woofs will never be quite parallel but intersect at various acute angles, giving rise to the typical 'watered' pattern, rather like the play of waves.

Graphically, such overlay figures may be achieved in various ways. Maughan S. Mason, for example, obtained random vortices by programming wave patterns into a computer (p. 72, top). The Kurt brothers and Paul Gysi dreamed up an intriguing device called the Linograph, which registers movement patterns from several pendulum tracks inclined at angles to one another (above and p. 72, bottom). Another readily available method is to overlay one screen with another transparent one (below).

Just place transparent page TR3 (Supplement) over the sister figures on this page and shift or turn it at random.

Beisp.56a.Scherzo v. L. Schlesinger aus London. (Wien, am 26. December 1832.)

Anagrams

The game of shifting around letters of one word or several in order to gain another word or phrase goes back to Lycophronus in the third century BC. Jewish Cabbalists gave further currency to it. Its culmination is reached in whole sentences that read the same backwards or forwards, such as 'able was I ere I saw Elba', or the Latin *Roma tibi subito motibus ibit amor* (from Rome love will come to you promptly with movement [emotion]). Other examples in various languages are shown in the five circles below. And at the right is a musical mirror piece, a scherzo by L. Schlesinger of London, dating back to 1832. Another variety of shaking up letters is the 'spoonerism' (named after the late Rev. W. A. Spooner), examples of which are 'thud and blunder', 'your show is slipping', etc.

74

96	11	89	68
88	69	91	16
61	86	18	99
19	98	66	81

1

```
SATOR
AREPO
TENET
OPERA
ROTAS
```

2

Magic Squares

Numbers compartmentalized into squares so as to give the same total for every rank and file, and often the diagonals as well, were known in China as long ago as 2400 BC. Engraved in metal or stone, they were carried as amulets or talismans. A Greek, Manuel Moschopulus, introduced them in Europe about AD 1300. One of the best known is a square of the fourth order in Albrecht Dürer's engraving *Melancolia*, a section of which is shown in Fig. 3.

The magic square in Fig. 1 works not only as shown, but even when it is turned upside down. The left-hand digits alone, moreover, form a magic square of their own, as do the right-hand digits alone, and again this holds true even when the whole thing is inverted. The Latin word-square SATOR – AREPO – TENET – OPERA – ROTAS (Fig. 2 – see also facing page) reads the same in all four cardinal directions, displaying double symmetry (but alas not diagonally!).

» Dennis sinned «

» Ma is as selfless as I am «

» Too hot to hoot «

» Trade ye no more moneyed art «

» Must sell at tallest sum «

» Lepers repel «

» Dog deifiers reified God «

» Madam I'm Adam «

3

The Paradox

Antinomies have troubled philosophers through the centuries. One of the disciples of Socrates inscribed on a tablet: 'The only sentence on this tablet is false', causing confusion among his fellows, for if the statement were true, it would be false, and if it were false, it would be correct. The famous statement that 'a Cretan said all Cretans are liars' is worth pondering – until one is bound to conclude that it is not possible to settle the question of whether the Cretan was lying just then or speaking the truth. Interesting contradictions between clashing theorems exist in mathematics and the natural sciences. Light, for example, may be explained in either corpuscular or wave terms, depending on the aspect being covered, even though the two theories conflict. Niels Bohr was fond of saying that 'the opposite of a true statement is a false statement, but the opposite of a profound truth may be another profound truth'.

In his *Transcendental Dialectics* Kant enumerates antinomies in which thesis clashes with antithesis, because the matters to which they refer are inherently contradictory. One such antinomy concerns our world in space and time. The thesis that the universe must have had a beginning and is bound to have an end fails to satisfy our reason – for how could the infinite cosmos arise from nothing and dissolve back into nothing? But if the thesis is not big enough, the antithesis – that the universe had no beginning and will have no end – is too big. Having no appropriate experience to draw on, we cannot imagine space and time without limits. We can conceive – indeed, require – the notion of a beginning, but we tend to think of space going on and on forever.

The German philosopher Friedrich von Schelling exclaimed: 'Why does something exist rather than nothing?' More than fifty million atoms can find room within the area of this full stop (·). Were we able to descend to one of these atoms, we should be facing a vast void, tantamount to nothingness. We might envisage the possibility of even this atom being subdivided, but we cannot conceive of it being dissolved into infinite nothingness without leaving a trace.

The idea of relativity is here taken to paradoxical lengths. In this pattern of multiple reflection and repetition of the same spatial situations, seen from both above and below, and also reversed from right to left, the late Dutch artist M. C. Escher presents one of his most baffling compositions. Curving walls and floors become interchangeable, and Escher's curious segmented creatures, climbing upwards, often seem to arrive at levels below those reached by their descending fellows.

THIS PAGE IS BLANK

The Apocryphal Dialogue of Xymmachus

by Robert Neumann, after Plato

XYMMACHUS: O thou my Socrates, I do encounter thee betimes in the market-place! Give me leave, then, to stroll by thy side towards Ilissus, as we push our way through the throng of hucksters!

SOCRATES: So be it! Dost thou not deem God-given the circumstance that the throng is all but impenetrable? And is it not therefore also God-given that in the presence of these hucksters we tarry here a while to hold converse?

XYMMACHUS: By Zeus, only a Boeotian would dispute thee.

SOCRATES: And what be the nature of this beast here proffered for sale?

XYMMACHUS: It is an ass, O Socrates!

SOCRATES: Truly, O Xymmachus, thou shinest in respect of recognition! I fancy I shall not be wide of the mark in maintaining that all other beasts, like unto this first one, that are all about proffered for sale may be described as donkeys?

XYMMACHUS: How else should I conclude, O Socrates?

SOCRATES: Most estimable! Were we now to suppose this ass to be able to understand our talk and to employ his tongue in the manner of men, wouldst thou deem it likely or otherwise that he would describe himself straightforwardly as a simple ass?

XYMMACHUS: I should deem it unlikely, O Socrates.

SOCRATES: And his vender, would he describe his ass as no better than those proffered all about?

XYMMACHUS: No man in his right senses would look for such a thing, O Socrates.

SOCRATES: What now, forsooth, if he were to describe his ass as a lion?

XYMMACHUS: Not I alone but all his rivals in the market-place would deem him a madman and bear witness against him.

SOCRATES: What then, forsooth, if there were a secret undertaking among all the asses, and among all the donkey drovers, that none should dispute another, if he chose to describe his ass as a lion, so long as all abided thereby? And what, forsooth, if thereafter *all* asses and donkey drovers described themselves as lions and lion-tamers?

XYMMACHUS: This, indeed, would be another matter!

SOCRATES: Thou deemest, therefore, that *the asinine, like the leonine is nought that is inherent in the thing, but licit or illicit according to an agreed nomenclature?*

XYMMACHUS: How could it be otherwise, O Socrates? But what if a true lion should venture among the donkeys?

SOCRATES: Once again, say I, O Xymmachus, thou shinest truly in respect of dialectics! But thinkest thou not that the asses described as lions would thereupon favour keeping the name of lion and describing the lone true lion as an ass?

XYMMACHUS: Indeed, the latter, O Socrates! They would call him an ass, but in the same breath they would take to their heels, lest they be eaten, and also lest they give occasion for comparison!

SOCRATES: And what of the beholder likely to compare – would they take to their heels before him as before the lion?

XYMMACHUS: Even so, and for the same reason!

SOCRATES: Those before whom they would not take to their heels, therefore, would be only other asses?

XYMMACHUS: Truly, thou sayest it!

SOCRATES: He that would compare – what should he do to keep them from taking to their heels and allow him to approach?

XYMMACHUS: Forsooth, he should clothe himself in the pelt of an ass! He should approach them with their own flag ahoist, so to speak, even as in war a ship seeking to strike a mortal blow sails *under a false flag!*

SOCRATES: Thou hast most estimably discovered this!

XYMMACHUS: How now, O Socrates, stands the ass as an entity in respect of the good and the fair? Does a preoccupation with asses come within the purview of the good and the fair? And if one who is good and fair fail to give asses a wide berth, be it his concern to strike a mortal blow against them, like unto that ship sailing under a false flag? Would it not be enough to tickle them a little?

SOCRATES: How now could the tickling of asses come within the purview of the good and the fair? Thou sayest it nay! Now as to the source of thy negation, lieth it with the tickling or with the asses?

XYMMACHUS: I understand thee not, O Socrates.

SOCRATES: Suppose now that he who is good and fair encounter a real lion – would he now venture to tickle such an one rather than to strike him a mortal blow?

XYMMACHUS: Surely the latter!

SOCRATES: Therefore lay the source of thy negation with the tickling! To strike mortal blows rather than to tickle must be the concern of the good and the fair, whatever the game. Hence it is meet that these misnamed asses be overtaken by the fate of lions. But how now, didst thou not ask whether a preoccupation with asses come within the purview of the good and the fair in the first place?

XYMMACHUS: I did so ask, by Zeus!

SOCRATES: Doth not a priest deal with still lowlier beasts? Doth he not, indeed, say sooth from their very dung?

XYMMACHUS: Thou sayest it, O Socrates, yet when he meet another priest, he smileth. Suppose, O Socrates, the priest err when he sayeth sooth from the dung!

SOCRATES: No matter, O my Xymmachus, if he but smile!

The Portrait

Each of the curious 'head men' above, taken from an old deck of cards, displays or conceals ten different faces. The single pair of eyes fits every newly appearing visage. It is another matter with the half-profile portrait Albrecht Dürer painted in 1526 of Jerome Holzschuher, who is shown gravely and critically scrutinizing the beholder. In defiance of the laws of perspective, his gaze seems never to leave us. We can observe a similar effect in photographs and on the television screen. When the eyes in the image are fixed on the camera lens, they seem to follow us around. In the absence of real depth, we supply a third dimension of our own, which roots us optically to a single spot in this imaginary space, even when we change our position in real space.

Try your hand at filling two of the ovals below with simple and schematic facial features – eyes, nose, mouth – *before* reading the upside-down legend at the bottom!

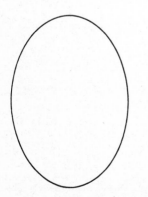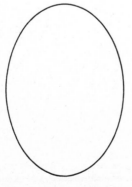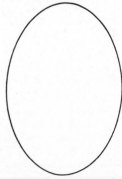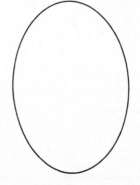

accurate rendering.
Use the remaining two ovals to give a more
hence we tend to give over most of the oval to it.
eyes, is by far the more expressive and interesting,

The lower half of the face, however, with the
of the nose should lie approximately halfway up.
outline face. Actually, the eyebrows and the root
Most people fail to give the right proportions to an

79

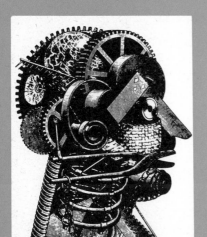

Draw round   and true   and there he stands   at Austerlitz   and Waterloo

A Squiggle, a Doodle . . .

. . . there's your noodle! Similar encouragements for the young limner will be found in many languages. They all have one thing in common – they begin with the two eye points, the first islands to emerge from what to a child must be an unknown vastness, the earliest reflection of understanding.

Wilhelm Busch's first three steps in drawing a caricature of Napoleon remain ambiguous. But just mark the eyes in any of them, and the hint of a face becomes unmistakable. The Age of the Baroque used illusion and ambiguity as stylistic means, and ever since, we find the portrait occasionally used as a double image, as in Poyet's late nineteenth-century engraving *The Inventor* (upper left) or the broadsheet of Napoleon (upper right).

In *Mao's Masses* (bottom), caricaturist Georg Rauch's fine pen teases our eyes, literally and metaphorically. Viewed at a distance, page 80 offers us two eye sockets from which to build up a death's head. But when we move it closer, a wealth of detail reveals something quite different. Yet even after we have recognized the lady at her dressing-table – the symbol of vanity – the skull re-emerges when we move back again.

A fascinating aspect of optical illusions is that we succumb to them, even when we understand how they work.

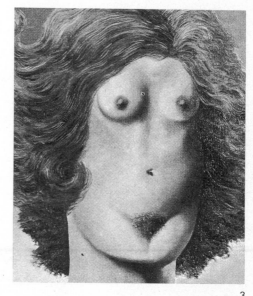

Fig. 1: Mae West, the movie actress, portrayed by Salvador Dali in 1936 as a surrealist salon.

Fig. 2: Anthropomorphic striptease — body mask worn by the music-hall artiste Choppy at the Concert Mayol in Paris.

Fig. 3: Le Viol, *1934, a blend of body and face by* Magritte.

Figs 4–6: *The Scholar, The Tradesman, The* Musician — *three caricatures from Zürich, about* 1850.

2

3

4

5

6

Folding Picture:
The Crone—Beauty Illusion

Fold back the upper left-hand corner of this
page against page 84, along the dashed line 1–1.
Then fold back the lower left-hand corner in
the same way, along the line 2–2. Next fold
back page 86 against page 85 in similar fashion,
first along line 3–3, and lastly line 4–4.
Depending on which feature you take to be
the eye, you will see the profile of a toothless
old woman, or a girl with a choker, her face
almost averted.

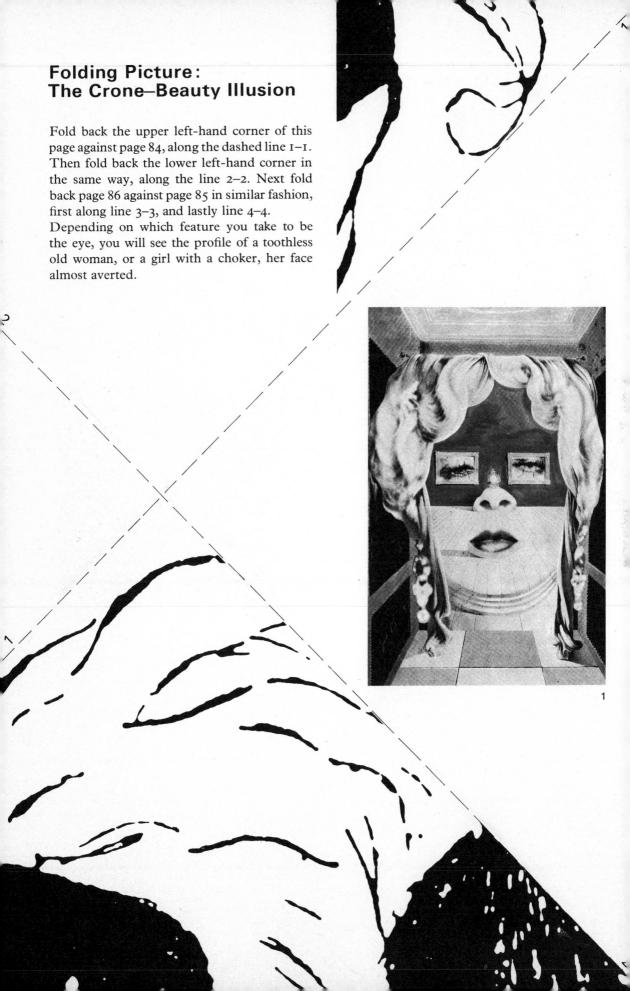

1

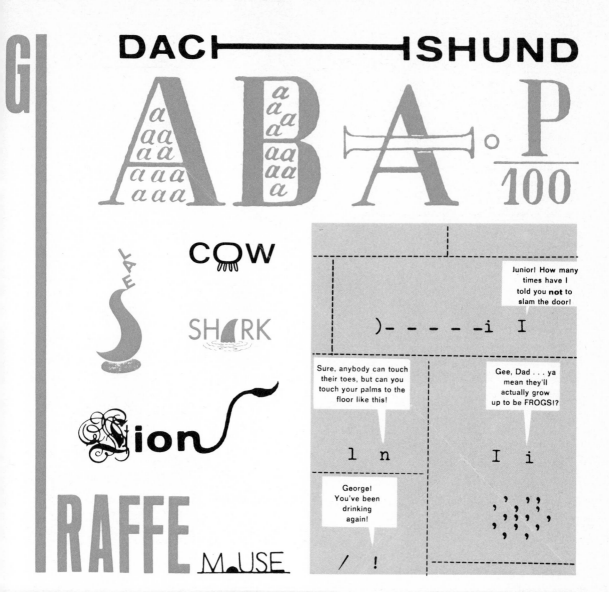

The Rebus

Each year during the Mardi Gras the notaries of Picardy in France used to compose satirical picture puzzles and puzzle pictures under the general title *De rebus quae geruntur*, literally, 'about things that are being done', meaning 'gossip that is going around'. This, some believe, is the origin of the word 'rebus' – a configuration of words and symbols that give new meaning when read literally or phonetically. A noted example, shown at the top: *Un grand AB, plein d'a-petits | A traversé par I | cent sous P*; or: *Un grand abbé, plein d'appétit, a traversé Paris sans souper*. A classic exchange in rebus form took place between Frederick the Great of Prussia and Voltaire. The king invited his guest as follows:

$$\frac{P}{\text{🖐 🖐}} \quad a \quad \frac{6}{100}$$

Deux mains sous P | a | cent sous six; or *Demain souper à Sanssouci* (Sanssouci being his palace at Potsdam). Voltaire gave a pithy reply: G a (*G grand, a petit*); or *J'ai grand appétit*.

In his book on poetry published in 1730, the German critic Johann Christoph Gottsched describes a French painting showing a dead abbot lying in a meadow. 'The artist, obeying I know not what unseemly custom, stuck a lily into the body's bare bottom.' Gottsched astutely deciphered the hidden meaning of this allegory: *Abbé mort en pré, au cul lys*; or read phonetically in Latin: *Habe mortem prae oculis* (keep death before thine eyes).

The 'calligrams' above characterize graphically the animals named. In the so-called 'Typewri-Toons', the sequence of typed characters seems meaningless – until one reads the captions!

Portraiture by typewriter.

Scripts and Pictorial Tricks

The art of writing took a long time to develop from mere 'art'. Man's original efforts to communicate were stories without words in which the picture situation or the things depicted were the carriers of information. In time, 'pictograms' were linked into 'words'; and long usage turned what had begun as a picture into an abstract shape that could be readily incised into a clay tablet with the point of a reed. Thus cuneiform writing was born, of the kind associated with the culture of Sumer, for example.

Artists in all ages have sought to travel the opposite road, using script for their capricious pictures, puzzles and visual puns. The portrait of Abraham Lincoln at the left uses the text of his famous Emanicipation Proclamation of 1863.

Fish's Night Song
by Christian Morgenstern
—

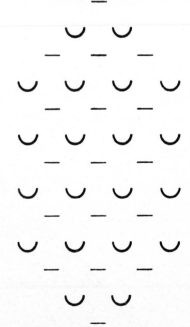

(considered by some to be the most profound poem in any language!)

FORSYTHIA

FORSYTHIA
OUT RACE SPRINGS YELLOW TELEGRAM HOPE INSISTS ACTION

Fun and Games with the ABC

It is sometimes contended that wordplay is simply a form of higher mathematics. Gerald Lynton Kaufman's *Geo-Metric Verse* (right) makes the contention plausible.

HERE IS VERSI-FORM DESIGNED IN A SHAPE WHICH BRINGS TO MIND, THAT WHEN PUT-TING THOUGHTS IN RHYME, YOU'RE SUPPOSED TO MEASURE TIME BUT THE MEASURE OF YOUR OWN, YOU SHOULD GLADLY LEAVE UNKNOWN; FOR THERE'S SCARCELY ANY DOUBT, THAT YOUR SAND IS RUNNING OUT.

'Mine is a long and a sad tale!' said the Mouse, turning to Alice, and sighing.

'It *is* a long tail, certainly,' said Alice, looking down with wonder at the Mouse's tail; 'but why do you call it sad?' And she kept on puzzling about it while the Mouse was speaking, so that her idea of the tale was something like this:——

```
        'Fury  said  to
          a mouse, That
            he  met in the
              house, "Let
                us both go
                  to  law: I
                  will  prose-
                  cute you.—
                Come, I'll
              take no de-
            nial:  We
          must  have
        the  trial;
      For  really
    this  morn-
    ing  I've
  nothing
  to do."
Said  the
    mouse to
      the  cur,
        "Such   a
          trial, dear
            sir, With
              no jury
              or judge,
                would
              be wast-
            ing our
          breath."
        "I'll   be
      judge,
    I'll be
  jury,"
  said
    cun-
      ning
        old
          Fury:
            "I'll
              try
                the
              whole
            cause,
          and
        con-
      demn
    you to
  death".'
```

A CONCRETE POEM

```
miniskirtminiskirt
miniskirtminiskirtmi
niskirtminiskirtminisk
irtminiskirtminiskirtmin
```

leglegleglegleglegleglegleg   leglegleglegleglegleglegleg

shoe   shoe

CUBICOUPLETS

A CUBE HAS SIX FACES A CUBE HAS SIX PLANES
RECTANGULAR SPACES FOR METRIC REFRAINS
FOR COUPLETS LIKE THESE WITH A RHYTHM, OF COURSE
TO BE READ AS YOU PLEASE EITHER DOWN OR ACROSS
EVERY FACE IS A SQUARE EVERY EDGE IS A LINE
TO HELP YOU COMPARE TO UNITE AND COMBINE
TWO PLANES AT A TIME FROM BEHIND OR BETWEEN
IN THIS CUBICAL RHYME WITH THE VERSES UNSEEN

A CUBE HAS SIX PLANES A CUBE HAS SIX FACES
FOR METRIC REFRAINS RECTANGULAR SPACES
WITH A RHYTHM, OF COURSE FOR COUPLETS LIKE THESE
EITHER DOWN OR ACROSS TO BE READ AS YOU PLEASE
EVERY EDGE IS A LINE EVERY FACE IS A SQUARE
TO UNITE AND COMBINE TO HELP YOU COMPARE
FROM BEHIND OR BETWEEN TWO PLANES AT A TIME
WITH THE VERSES UNSEEN IN THIS CUBICAL RHYME

The Man Who Carried His Hat

by Carlo Manzoni

I can't tell you when I saw him for the first time. It must have been a very, very long time ago. Perhaps ten years, perhaps twenty, perhaps even three hundred. It's hard to judge time, when you think back. And when it's a matter of little importance, it's even harder – almost impossible, I should say.

Things just get away from one, that's all. All that remains is a vague impression, as though what one seeks to remember is seen through a dense fog, barely perceptible. One simply can't judge how long ago it was.

Then I saw him again a few times, and that I remember quite plainly. Once he stood by a fence, another time he sat on a bench, and again he was leaning on a bar with his elbows. And each time he carried a hat in his hand.

Sometimes the hat was grey, sometimes brown – but it most definitely was a hat.

What a thing habit is! Not habit, really, but how things persist. I'm not expressing myself well, and I don't think I can explain what I'm trying to say. We often lack the right words to explain something, and there it hangs suspended in the air, without our being able to capture it.

Actually, the man was of no importance whatever to me. He was simply some unknown person, like so many others, quite nondescript and uninteresting. The kind one doesn't give a second glance, is what I'm trying to say. Possibly I wouldn't even have noticed him but for the hat in his hand, and I wouldn't have remembered him at all, any more than I would a thousand other people I've run into, once or more than once.

The hat as such didn't mean anything either. Hats seldom do. We see thousands of hats, and personally I must have seen every kind and variety known. But all these hats too just vanish from our view without leaving a trace.

Two trivial things, in other words, a man and a hat. It's not that the man meant nothing at all – after all, all men have some significance – but to me he was simply an unknown man like countless others who had no business in my life.

I saw him walk beside a woman, and he carried his hat in his hand. I saw him get off a tram, and he carried his hat in his hand. Initially, the impression of this man with a hat in his hand didn't want to stick in my memory. It was an image that came and went without leaving a trace. In time, however, it did leave a trace.

I began to watch him when he passed my window, his hat in his hand. That's the way it goes – when you see something again and again, you begin to observe it, and then something gets inside you. It takes hold of you and doesn't leave you alone.

I began to ask myself, not who the man was, but why he kept carrying his hat in his hand. I began to speculate that he must have a hatrack at home but probably never used it and instead put his hat on a table or chair.

Next I thought that his hat must be too tight or too wide. I began to scrutinize his thick shock of hair, to estimate the size of his head, to visualize him with his hat on his head.

By and by I got used to the man with the hat in his hand. I knew the precise time when he would pass my house and when he would enter the bar. I grew certain that his hat would be in his hand whenever I caught sight of him.

One day he gave me a real start. The hat wasn't grey any longer, but brown and brand-new.

New thoughts began to torment me. I imagined the man picking out a new hat. Looking at himself in the mirror, with the new hat, in his hand rather than on his head.

Not a hat that fitted his head but rather one that harmonized with his appearance. It didn't matter whether it was too tight or too wide. The old hat still put in an appearance now and then, when the weather was bad. But even then the man went bareheaded, hugging the wall, to protect himself against the rain. . . .

I tried to decipher the expression on his face, whenever I saw him, but he just looked like any man passing me by. I'm sure he never devoted any thought to his hat, to which he scarcely even gave a glance, at least not that I noted. If he harboured any prejudice against head-coverings, it certainly never showed.

He seemed completely indifferent to his hat. One day, in the bar, it dropped from his hand. He stooped to pick it up, brushed off the dust and patted it back into shape with a few slight and well-chosen movements.

Everything concerning this hat now comes back to me. I recall a hot summer afternoon, when the man fanned himself with his hat. I also remember an occasion on the tram, when he slipped his ticket behind the hatband.

I recall having decided one day to challenge the man and to ask him why he always carried his hat in his hand. I also recall changing my mind. Possibly, I thought, I might be touching a sore spot. I imagined the man first looking at me and then at his hat, then bursting into tears, crushing his hat in his hands, throwing it into the street and running away from me, amid sobs.

So I did nothing.

And then, one day, the unexpected happened. To this day I don't really understand how such a thing could happen. Indeed, sometimes I wonder whether my senses didn't deceive me. Anyway, I saw the man pass me with his hat on his head. He was wearing the brown one. The grey one he carried in his hand.

I Mean What I Say What I Mean

from *Through the Looking-Glass* by Lewis Carroll

'. . . Tell me your name and your business.'

'My *name* is Alice, but——'

'It's a stupid name enough!' Humpty Dumpty interrupted impatiently. 'What does it mean?'

'*Must* a name mean something?' Alice asked doubtfully.

'Of course it must,' Humpty Dumpty said with a short laugh: '*my* name means the shape I am – and a good handsome shape it is, too. With a name like yours, you might be any shape, almost. . . . Here's a question for you. How old did you say you were?'

Alice made a short calculation, and said 'Seven years and six months.'

'Wrong!' Humpty Dumpty exclaimed triumphantly. 'You never said a word like it!'

'I thought you meant "How old *are* you?"' Alice explained.

'If I'd meant that, I'd have said it. . . . When *I* use a word,' Humpty Dumpty said, in rather a scornful tone, 'it means just what I choose it to mean – neither more nor less.'

'The question is,' said Alice, 'whether you *can* make words mean so many different things.' . . .

'When I make a word do a lot of work . . .' said Humpty Dumpty, 'I always pay it extra. . . . Ah, you should see 'em come round me of a Saturday night,' [he] went on, wagging his head gravely from side to side, 'for to get their wages, you know.' . . .

'You seem very clever at explaining words, Sir,' said Alice. 'Would you kindly tell me the meaning of the poem called "Jabberwocky"?' . . .

'Plenty of hard words there,' [said Humpty Dumpty]. '*Brillig* means four o'clock in the afternoon – the time when you begin *broiling* things for dinner.'

'That'll do very well,' said Alice: 'and *slithy*?'

'Well, *slithy* means "lithe and slimy". "Lithe" is the same as "active". You see it's like a portmanteau – there are two meanings packed up into one word.'

'I see it now,' Alice remarked thoughtfully: 'and what are *toves*?'

'Well, *toves* are something like badgers – they're something like lizards – and they're something like corkscrews.'

'They must be very curious-looking creatures.'

'They are that,' said Humpty Dumpty; 'also they make their nests under sun-dials – also they live on cheese.'

'And what's to *gyre* and to *gimble*?'

'To *gyre* is to go round and round like a gyroscope. To *gimble* is to make holes like a gimlet.'

'And *the wabe* is the grass-plot round a sun-dial, I suppose?' said Alice, surprised at her own ingenuity.

'Of course it is. It's called *wabe* you know, because it goes a long way before it, and a long way behind it——'

'And a long way beyond it on each side,' Alice added.

'Exactly so. Well then, *mimsy* is "flimsy and miserable" (there's another portmanteau for you). And a *borogrove* is a thin shabby-looking bird with its feathers sticking out all round – something like a live mop.'

'And then *mome raths*?' said Alice. 'I'm afraid I'm giving you a great deal of trouble.'

'Well, a *rath* is a sort of green pig: but *mome* I'm not certain about. I think it's short for "from home" – meaning that they'd lost their way, you know.'

'And what does *outgrabe* mean?'

'Well, *outgribing* is something between bellowing and whistling, with a kind of sneeze in the middle: however, you'll hear it done, maybe – down in the wood yonder – and, when you've once heard it, you'll be *quite* content. . . .'

'Twas brillig, and the slithy toves
Did gyre and gimble in the wabe;
All mimsy were the borogroves,
And the mome raths outgrabe.

Horizontal versus Vertical

A vertically striped area looks wide, while one that is horizontally striped looks high.

When the eye fastens on a hatched shape, it slips easily along the light and dark tracks, while going crosswise it must move from light to dark and back again. We do not actually notice the additional effort in this 'ladder-climbing', but it does affect the brain's ability to estimate distances. Sliding along the stripes gives a lower value, stumbling across alternating bands a higher one.

Thus the subdivided distance A–B (right) seems greater than the empty stretch B–C. This effect was known to Romanesque architects. In the cathedral at Siena, for example, horizontal striping enhances the height of the columns (bottom right).

It is not all that easy to make a stack of coins as high as it is wide. If asked to judge which of the two piles illustrated is equal in height and width, most people would choose the one on the right – but measurement will show that it is in fact the left-hand pile.

The areas of the three figures below are the same, but the one on the right looks taller, the one on the left wider.

Perception and Reality

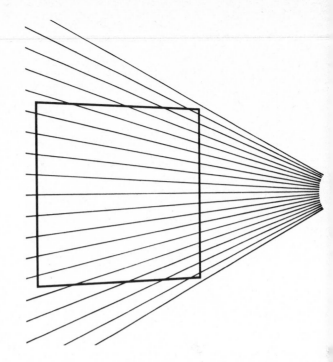

When a simple geometric figure is placed over a perspective grid it loses some of its inherent properties and becomes distorted through the resultant depth effect. In order to restore its original character we actually have to falsify it. The left side of the apparent square (right) is about $\frac{1}{8}$ in. longer than the right side!

We are so accustomed to making correct estimates of size in pictures in which the space is drawn in perspective that we are almost compelled to scale up the four figures of a businessman shown below against a perspective grid, although they are all of the same size. The one 'farthest away' on the right looks to be about twice as tall as his colleague on the extreme left. A study of important public occasions is sometimes instructive. If the most important

dignitary appearing happens to be of small stature, it is quite likely that an effort will be made to enhance the show of power by various optical tricks. He may be standing on an invisible platform that makes him look taller, or he may pick even shorter persons to stand near him. If for any reason such expedients are impracticable, the background decorations may be so designed as to make him the focus of attention.

Lines that converge toward a vanishing point in the middle of a picture, as on the right, are particularly effective in causing seeming distortion. The white bars between the rails are all of the same size.

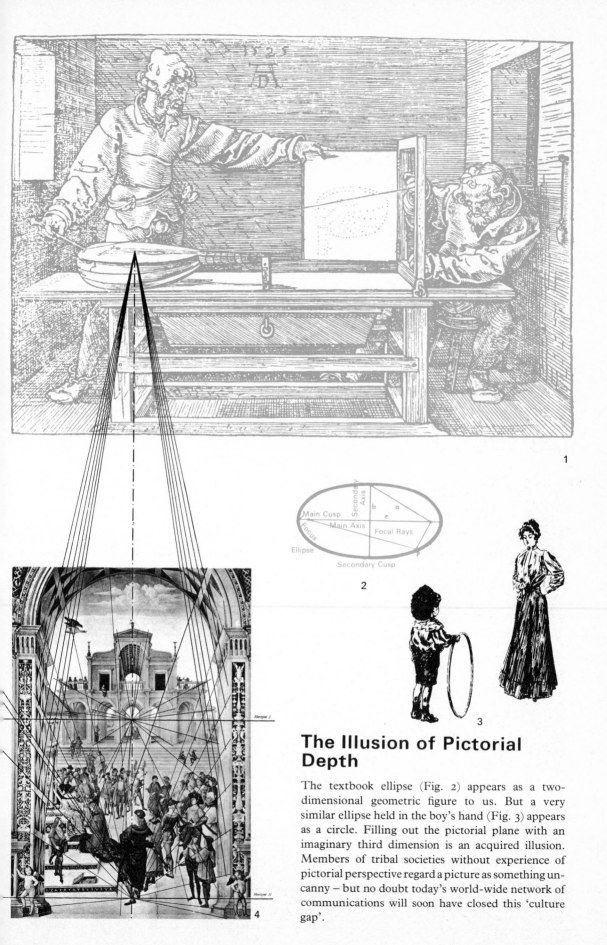

1

2

Main Cusp · Secondary Axis · b a · c · Main Axis · Focal Rays · Focus · Ellipse · Secondary Cusp · p

3

4

Horizon I

Horizon II

The Illusion of Pictorial Depth

The textbook ellipse (Fig. 2) appears as a two-dimensional geometric figure to us. But a very similar ellipse held in the boy's hand (Fig. 3) appears as a circle. Filling out the pictorial plane with an imaginary third dimension is an acquired illusion. Members of tribal societies without experience of pictorial perspective regard a picture as something uncanny – but no doubt today's world-wide network of communications will soon have closed this 'culture gap'.

5

7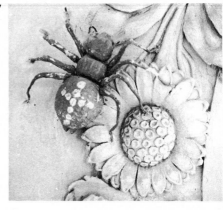

8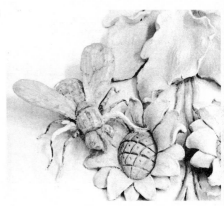

6

Trompe-l'oeil and Perspective

Albrecht Dürer wrote in 1525 (Fig. 1): 'Prick thou points in the panel where thou seest the outlines and parts of the lute / Thereupon join thou all the dots on the panel with proper lines / And thou shalt see what cometh thereof.'

The art of perspective represents a new relation of man and his environment. What our eyes take for granted may not be comprehensible to eyes that have been exposed to different experiences.

A correct approach to perspective was achieved only in the Renaissance. Pinturicchio (1454–1513) was already experimenting with it, using a bit of trickery with the vanishing points (Fig. 4, *Frederick III Crowning Enea Silvio Piccolomini Poet Laureate*, Siena Cathedral). There is an unbroken tradition of entertaining and often profound illusion and ambiguity that leads from the Baroque Age to our own times, as exemplified by the pseudo-perspective of the choir screen in the collegiate church at Einsiedeln, Switzerland (Fig. 6), the realistic stucco work at Steinhausen (Figs 7 and 8), and Magritte's picture within a picture (Fig. 5).

different places. Hogarth's lampoon is studded with errors, but since we are so accustomed to pictures drawn in correct perspective, we readily recognize the various distortions. Escher's pictorial meditation is marked by a spatial construction that accords with our visual habits, hence we have some difficulty in groping our way toward the three different vantage points of the picture.

In essence every work of art constitutes an illusion. The artist cannot really communicate 'reality' and he has no such intention. In his works he proffers his visual and intellectual world to ours. The images of these worlds are not true analogues of nature but merely resemble it. Sir Ernst Gombrich, in *Art and Illusion*, has dealt with these profound and interesting problems with much insight.

Paradoxical Aspects of Depth

Below: Autre Monde, *wood engraving by M. C. Escher, 1947.*

Facing page: False Perspective, *engraving by Hogarth, 1754.*

The eye sleeps until the mind wakes it with a question.

ARABIAN PROVERB

Both pictures exploit the illusion of depth to depict contradictions of space and time. Parts of the pictures are simultaneously located at

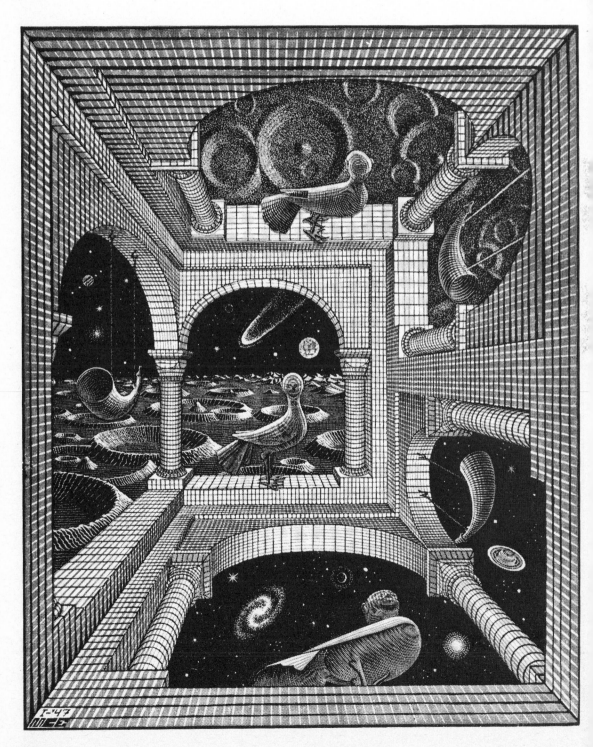

Illusion and Point of Vantage

Top, facing page: Monsters on the march? Oil-well pumps in California.

Bottom, facing page: Who is touching the ball? Two shots taken at the same instant at right-angles to each other.

Right: Are there six solid objects on the chessboard or only four? Two shots of the same arrangement.

The two pairs of photographs come from the Swiss Federal Polytechnic and were designed for police instruction. They show how hard it may be to evaluate even eye-witness testimony properly, to rule out unconscious subjective error. We tend to take a plausible grouping at face value, rarely considering other possible interpretations, especially if these are bizarre.

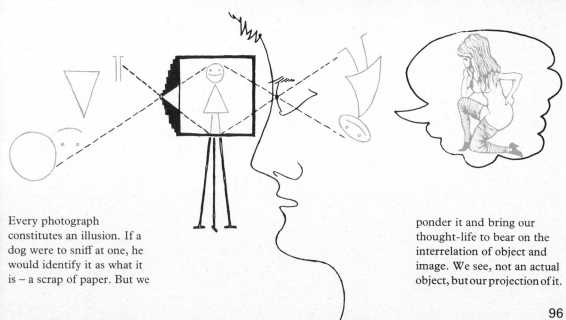

Every photograph constitutes an illusion. If a dog were to sniff at one, he would identify it as what it is – a scrap of paper. But we ponder it and bring our thought-life to bear on the interrelation of object and image. We see, not an actual object, but our projection of it.

FOR THE SOUL

TAKES ON

THE COLOUR

OF ITS IDEAS.

MARCUS AURELIUS

CHARACTER IS
GUIDED BY
THE NATURE OF
THINGS MOST OFTEN
ENVISAGED.

depending on the proportion of distribution, either black or white functions as "background" and the other as "pattern". But as the two come into balance, this becomes more and more difficult. Often such a distribution seems to our eyes to reverse in a matter of seconds.'

Well now, does the zebra have black stripes on a white ground or white stripes on a black ground? In fact its basic coloration is dark, and the white stripes represent a relatively recent evolutionary acquisition.

Top illustration: Study for Slave Market, *by Salvador Dali. Figures beneath a round arch, or a bust of Voltaire?*

Centre illustration: Geometric pattern or name of Mexican mountain? To aid comprehension, lay strips of dark paper along the top and bottom edges.

Interchanging Images

Dark colour obtrudes more than white, hence at first glance we are likely to see the figure at left as a vase, and only on second glance do we note that its contours are profiles.

In his 1957 print, above, M. C. Escher tried to give equal optical weight to the light and the dark figurations. Yet we are unable to perceive them both at the same time, for we can see one only against the background of the other. In the letter illusion at lower left, our first impulse is to make sense of it from the dark islands and it is only then that we perceive three capitals that form the first three letters of the word ITALY.

'Fortunately for our peace of mind,' writes W. Metzger, 'reversing patterns occur only rarely in nature. One of the few examples is the zebra with its coat evenly divided between black and white. Usually,

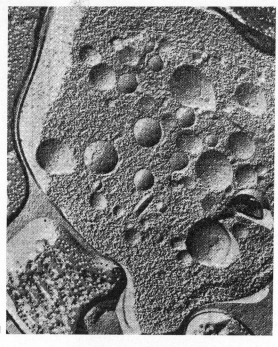

1

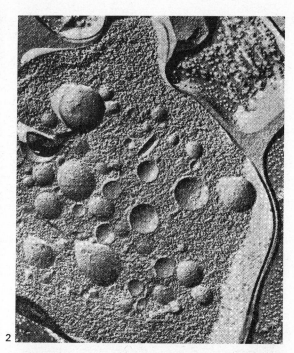

2

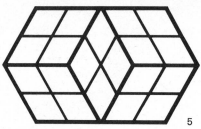

3

5

Dimples or Wens?

Figs 1 and 2 are actually the same picture, in one case rotated through 180°. The shot happens to be an electron-micrograph of thrombocytes prepared by the freeze-etching process. When we take a close look, we note that the depressions in the left-hand picture have turned into protuberances in the right-hand one, and vice versa.

The same effect is noted in Figs 3 and 4, which show two fossil ammonites and moulds made from them. You may think you know beyond any doubt which is which, but just turn the page and your certainty goes out the window – it is simply impossible to tell. Your eyes can see the objects both ways, as they can the so-called Wundt Prism (Fig. 5). Sometimes the left side is seen to be hollow, sometimes the right side.

4

Convex – Concave

M. C. Escher's well-known print shows concavity on the right, convexity on the left. Both meet in the middle, where rationality ends and the floor becomes ceiling, and inside outside.

Viewing in perspective is a learned trick, a form of acculturation. Children, like members of tribal societies, do not necessarily see representations of objects as three-dimensional. They rather tend to equate the seen thing with the felt thing, however. Right-handedness gives rise to light incidence from upper left, as most schools and offices will exemplify, and the notion that shadows of objects should fall toward the lower right becomes firmly entrenched in nearly all of us. In consequence, when we see an unfamiliar picture, we tend first of all to see shapes and forms that would account for shadows at lower right. Craters in moonscapes have not yet become everyday sights and when we look at pictures of them, they often tend suddenly to 'pop out'.

a profile that faces right with the left hand. Conversely, right-handers see a duck.

We also show a directional bias in our postures and movements. Right-handers like to turn toward the right – e.g. they nearly always take the right-hand flight of two symmetrical stairways. We know beyond question that, despite their best efforts, even experienced alpine guides invariably veer toward the right in fogs, when their wonted landmarks vanish. People traversing unfamiliar terrain, such as deserts or arctic wastes, without a compass, may wander in circles, to their peril and complete frustration.

Heinrich Wölfflin, an eminent art historian, studied the effects of reversing a picture. One might think that a harmoniously composed picture would be so self-contained that reversing it would scarcely impair, let alone destroy, its effect. What actually happens can be readily learned with the help of a mirror, or by projecting a slide the other way round. The example here chosen is Rembrandt's etching of three oak trees, one of his most popular landscapes. In the proper version, at the top of the page, the group of trees, on the right, accents the whole composition, for the effect of any picture is always largely determined by the right side, the finale, so to speak, for the eyes moving from left to right. In the reversal, underneath the top picture, the trees lose their importance and the eyes rest on the expanse of the countryside. Movements running from lower left to upper right are commonly sensed as ascending, while the opposite direction connotes a fall.

Left and Right

Right, *droit, rechts* – in English, French and German these three words, all meaning the same thing, have the secondary (or possibly primary) meaning of correct, proper, lawful.

On the other hand, left, *gauche, links* have secondary meanings of clumsy, illegitimate, sinister (the precise Latin analogue) and even evil.

When we examine our bodies carefully we note that despite their apparent symmetry, they exhibit a distinct morphological and functional bias toward the right side or the left.

We may think of a face as perfectly even, but actually the two sides of it differ markedly. The French actress Brigitte Bardot is shown at left centre as she actually looks, while at the top is her 'left face' (i.e. the left side, reversed, replacing the normal right side) and at the bottom her 'right face'. You can readily create such faces with any photograph, with the help of a small hand mirror.
Dr Werner Wolff, who has studied the subject, says that the right side is the positive, affirmative 'day face', representing the traits we consciously seek to project in life. In the left, demoniac or 'night face' individuality gives way to our hidden, unconscious aspects.

The right side is closer to the normal image, more developed, expressive, masculine, while the left is softer, less distinct, more feminine. This may well be the reason why painters and sculptors prefer to show the left profile in women and the right side in men.

These differences are reflected in the brain. Since the nerve paths cross over, the left hemisphere controls the right side of the face, and the left hemisphere is the seat of rational awareness. The right hemisphere, which controls the left side of the face, remains incompletely explored, but it undoubtedly has more to do with the unconscious.

Ancient philosophers were already concerned with the question of 'handedness'. Plato thought that man's basic predisposition was ambidextrous. Paul Sarasin, a Basle anthropologist and historian, studying stone tools of the Paleolithic age, concluded that their wielders were equally divided among right-handers and left-handers. It is only civilization with its increasingly sophisticated technology that seems to have awarded preference to the right hand, perhaps because of the fortuitous adaptation of a whole series of utensils. Over the millennia, training and tradition may have forced the lefties into the right-hand mould. This functional asymmetry extends even to 'eyedness'. Two in every three people are right-eyed. Unequivocally left-oriented subjects, hands and eyes, usually see the figure on the facing page at first as a rabbit, because they tend to draw recognize or perceive anything – we are 'cerebrally blind'. Identification takes place in the optical memory centre, represented in the picture (left) by the gentlemen beneath the dome of the *camera obscura*. Here perception is interpreted, conclusions are reached, action is decided upon. Most illusions go back to misjudgments by this 'committee', which is often arch-conservative and tries to subsume the new, 'unseen', under some old familiar pattern.

Impressions from the outside world help us build up the abundant store of our memory field. In dreams, the brain blends memory fragments into autonomous inner processes that have a verisimilitude bordering on reality. But we can also project memory fragments into what we actually see with open eyes. The ink-blot pictures of the Rorschach Test (pp. 108/9, centre) serve to reflect the inner imagery we have stored up.

Seen through the camera's single eye, a hollow mould of a plaster cast (upper right) gives us no chance to perceive depth properly with our stereoscopically arranged double eyes. Even when the mould is tilted, we still 'see' a normal face bulging out. It requires real effort to perceive the mould as concave, although this becomes a bit easier with one eye closed.

Faith, comparison, recognition and knowledge all serve to intermingle the poles of the inner and outer worlds, but puzzling aspects remain, as in the story of a blind friend, related by Einstein, who was taking a walk in the country with him on a hot summer day. Einstein said he wished he had a glass of milk to drink. 'Milk?' said the friend. 'I can understand drink, but what's milk?' 'It's a white fluid,' Einstein replied. 'I know what a fluid is,' said the blind man, 'but what's white?' 'It's the colour of a swan's feather,' said Einstein. 'I know what a feather is,' said the blind friend, 'but what's a swan?' 'A bird with a curving neck,' said Einstein and, losing patience, seized his friend's arm and held it straight out. 'That's straight,' he said and, bending the arm at the elbow, 'that's curved or bent!' 'Ah,' said the blind man, 'now I know what you meant by milk!'

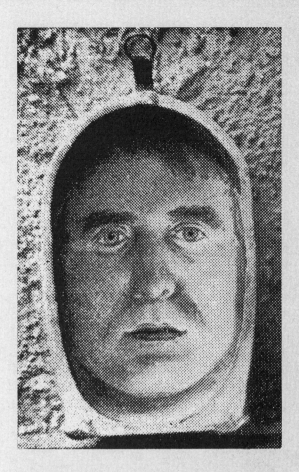

Object   Light Stimulus   Eye

Optical Memory Centre

Visual Centre

The Mind's Eye

When Fritz Kahn was reproached for an inaccuracy in his representation of the atom, he shrewdly replied: 'It may be wrong, but it's understandable.' Our representation of the process of perception (above) is also a crude simplification – but it does show that the seen thing and our internalization of it are as different as the painter's model and the painted picture he makes of her.

Our eyes inaugurate the process that begins with seeing and continues by way of recognition to cognition. When we say 'I'll see', we mean that we shall consider. We speak of insight, foresight, hindsight. We hold 'views' – indeed we may have a 'world view' or as the Germans put it, a *Weltanschauung*, a philosophy. Words such as 'view' and 'vision' all go back to the Greek word *eidos*, which can mean many things, from idea (virtually the same word) to image, shape, form, even dream or illusion.

Reports about the surfaces of objects are transmitted by the eye to the visual centre. When that is defective, we can no longer spectacles before my eyes, I continue to see them as the same spatial object, even though the image it forms on my retina undergoes many changes in size and perspective. Our sensory and supportive resources actually perform prodigies of stereometric adjustment and correction that are so commonplace that we no longer marvel at them.

All these exceedingly complex allowances almost certainly subserve the goal of what is called 'objective constancy', which satisfies our need to identify a given object under all conceivable conditions of perception. Overall, this mechanism underlies, indeed probably predicates, the even subtler processes of purely mental abstraction. The process of singling out an object's inherent properties from its fortuitous background is simply extended to whole groups of objects, as a beginning.

Tradition is yet another element that led to the fulguration terminating in man. Many of the higher animals do have traditions, but these are invariably object-bound, since animals lack the capacity for free symbolization. That may be the reason that traditional knowledge is non-cumulative in all animals known to us. Of course other non-specific and pre-existing faculties played a part in the genesis of man – a precise central representation of spatial events, the ability to move under volitional control, a capacity for mimicry, etc. The three abilities mentioned above, however, suffice to account for the creation of an altogether new complex of action not shared by any animal, namely the capacity for conceptual thought. Exploration and self-exploration result in elements that are essential to conceptual thinking. But without abstraction and tradition they can never become the common property of society. Only complete integration can set the scene for free symbolization, syntactical and evaluative language and thus the cumulation of supra-individual knowledge, skills and motivations, which we are accustomed to describe collectively as civilization.

With this fulguration, an entirely new biological quality of man came into being. A new type of heredity has arisen, which amounts to nothing less than the much-disputed inheritance of acquired characteristics. The invention of the bow and arrow confer their advantages not merely to the inventor's progeny – they

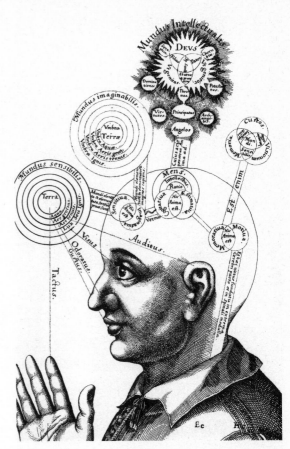

A Universe within the Mind. *Illustration by the English doctor Robert Fludd, seventeenth century.*

come into the free possession of all mankind, which may indeed claim the insights of any great man as its heritage, even when the great man is younger than his beneficiaries. The mind of man is unprecedented and immortal.

The Mind of Man

by Konrad Lorenz

Medieval mystics called the unpredictable creation of the unprecedented *fulgoratio*. They had in mind, of course, the lightning bolt dispatched by the Creator to ripen growth into existence. But the term is peculiarly apt for real events in which the unprecedented is created without violating natural law. When we see an unexpected flash in some experimental system, our immediate thought is of a short-circuit! Somewhere, we conclude, the insulation has broken down and two systems that were formerly separate are now in contact. This is how the new may come into being. We find fulgurations of this type at every turn in the course of evolution. Life itself is probably the most important of such lightning flashes. In any definition of life, one has to take note not only of vital functions in terms of energy and cognition, but also of the structure of the long-chained molecules of the genome that subserve the acquisition and storage of information.

And what about another great discontinuity in the stratification of real existence, the step that leads from animal up to man? Did this basic differentiation also arise from a unique fulguration, in which altogether new properties arose from the integration of previously independent systems? I believe this indeed to have been the case, that the qualities and capacities characterizing man as a cultural being may be explained by a combination of structures and functions that pre-existed in higher animals. Let me mention a few examples.

The characteristic curiosity attitude of animals is manifested in the successive display toward an unknown object of a whole range of behaviours available to an animal. A juvenile raven will treat an unknown object first as a mortal enemy, next as a prize to be killed, then as food and lastly as indifferent material with which real food may be covered up and hidden. When the bird tests out food ingestion movements with the object, this does not necessarily connote hunger. It simply wants to discover whether the object is edible. It proceeds in a strictly experimental way.

In the case of man and manlike creatures, which make pre-eminent use of their hands in exploring the outside world and thus keep them almost constantly in view, we may well imagine that the hand itself becomes an object of curiosity, giving rise to the process of self-exploration so characteristic of man. And when a primate notes that his hand, grasping an object, is itself a real object in the world, a process is set in motion in which 'grasping' is not merely a physical act but becomes a mental concept.

Another perceptual abstraction, more particularly in the area of configuration or *gestalt*, which has also come to be regarded as specifically human and which has evolved quite independently of explorative behaviour, concerns the abstraction of constancy from a range of perceptions. For example, we develop fixed concepts of inherent colour that remain unaffected by the fortuitous shifts in illumination. We see a piece of paper as white, whether it is actually seen in 'white' daylight or in the rosy hues of sunset or in the yellowish glow from an incandescent bulb. A complex computer mechanism in the brain 'calculates' the reflective properties of the paper from the colour of the incident illumination and the wavelengths actually reflected from the object at the moment.

Another constancy phenomenon concerns the shape of objects. As my hand turns my

Dr Wilder Penfield's representation of brain localization shows that some parts of the body are grossly over-represented, in keeping with their importance to our everyday functioning.

The Restless Mind

'Regard a wall grown spotted with damp or a stone of irregular tint. If thou seekest to devise backgrounds, thou shalt eftsoons find in them the most glorious landscapes.' Thus Leonardo da Vinci. Whatever comes before our eyes we are wont to classify with and assign to familiar images. We see figures chasing one another in the drifting clouds, the flickering flames, the abstract texture of a wall (above).

When we present a totally neutral pattern to the eye, say a grid of dots devoid of all meaning (right), we catch ourselves after a while trying to group the dots into rows and squares, crosses and diagonals.

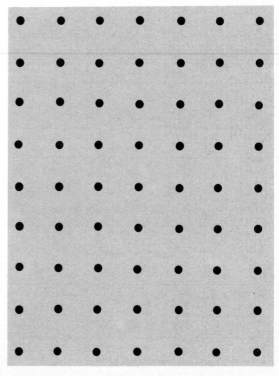

> Sometime we see a cloud that's dragonish,
> A vapour sometime like a bear or lion,
> A towered citadel, a pendent rock,
> A forkéd mountain, or blue promontory
> With trees upon't, that nod unto the world
> And mock our eyes with air.

SHAKESPEARE, ANTONY AND CLEOPATRA, IV. xii

Line

Cartoonists would have a hard time, were it not for our eyes' propensity to be ever on the lookout for 'context'. Often we need but the barest hint and our minds will supply the whole picture – or at least what we want to see. A single line may be enough to set the imagination turning over and coming up with a scene. It can serve as the horizon, a weapon, a washing-line, a staff in musical notation, a border or division, an essential part in a fraction – you name it. Some lines below have been left blank, to exercise your imagination. The German word for line, *Strich*, is missing after *auf dem* . . . , but *auf dem Strich* does not mean merely 'on the line': in the vernacular it signifies 'hustling', being a prostitute.

auf dem...

Lines That Aren't There

A closely spaced row of fine dots is readily seen as a line, the points serving as 'bridges' for our eyes. Such bridging can fool even scientists, as happened to the astronomer Schiaparelli in 1888, when he thought he saw lines on Mars through his telescope (Fig. 2), thus giving rise to the famous and spurious

1

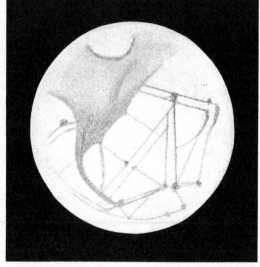

2

'Canals of Mars'. Actually, astronomers have since ancient times joined groups of stars into 'constellations', to which they attach names. Fig. 1 shows an old Chinese representation of the Big Dipper.

. . . and Figures Too

Our eyes also seek to combine into meaningful images what at first blush may look like a heap of unrelated spots. Sometimes a meaning really resides in the conglomeration, as in the terrier, above. In other instances, as in the engraving by Bracelli, below, which dates back to 1624, we readily accept the artist's meaning, as expressed in his title, *Erotic Temple*.

Horseman and Mount

For much imaginary work was there;
Conceit deceitful, so compact, so kind,
That for Achilles' image stood his spear
Gripped in an arméd hand; himself behind
Was left unseen, save to the eye of mind:
  A hand, a foot, a face, a leg, a head,
  Stood for the whole to be imaginéd.

SHAKESPEARE, THE RAPE OF LUCRECE

As you regard this figure, note the loss of your naïve innocence as it occurs! At first you will see what looks like merely a meaningless array of patches. But if you turn the page 90° to the right, you begin to see some of the patches as meaningful groups. And once they all come together to form a horseman astride his mount, this meaning will become so fixed in your mind that you can scarcely recreate the original random aggregation that greeted your 'unsophisticated' eyes. Eskimos seem particularly able to pick out hidden figures in confusing pell-mell patterns, as has been shown in tests of subjects from varying cultural backgrounds. People who can pick out a polar bear in the icy wastes despite his white camouflage seem to acquire a greater capacity for resolving optical impressions the rest of us find hard to distinguish.

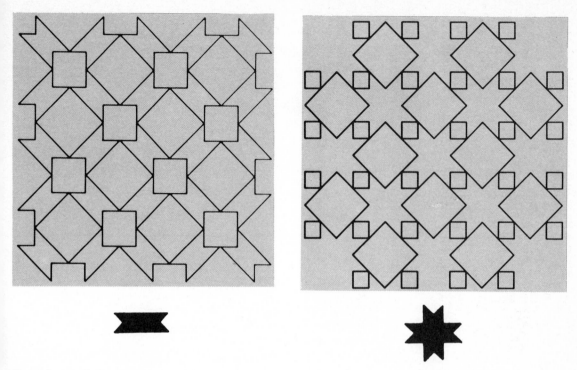

Seeing Shapes

When we look at a picture, we quickly recognize what is familiar to us; and we are more likely to grow familiar with simple rather than complex configurations. Closed and readily perceived shapes get preference over open and limitless forms and areas; and when we have noted the simple figures, we are often led to believe that we have 'seen it all'. Yet we may completely overlook essential elements. For example, the pattern at upper left is really made up of the spindle-shape shown below it, and the one at upper right of the cruciform star, again shown below.

The figures below mislead us, like puzzle pictures, into seeing only the obvious. It becomes far harder to 'peel out' the numerals hidden in the clouds.

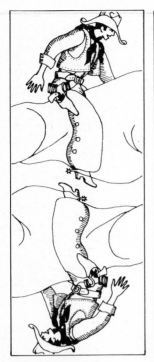

Intelligence Test?

1.   Trace the oblong with the two cowboys at upper left and try to mount them on the two bulls.

2.   Find the five-pointed star in the mosaic at left.

3.   Among the diagrams below, find three equal hexagons, three equal boxes and three equal oblongs with a corner pointing downward.

If you can do this fast you're bright, if you can't you're dull! But really, now, we should be deluding ourselves, if we believed that we can measure our minds and alertness in such casual fashion! To a professional proof-reader, the tiniest typographical error leaps to the eye, while the ordinary reader just brushes past it without even noticing it. Our senses cope day after day with the things in our personal world, and in consequence we tend to see only what affects us, ignoring all else.

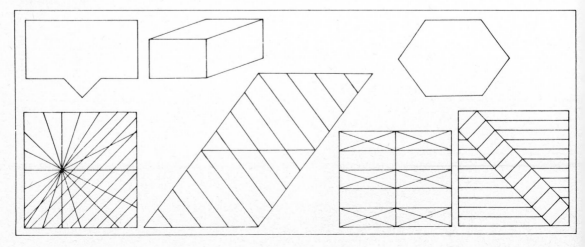

The Crazy Room

The two pictures at left show the same room with the same two people, a father and his son. The walls of the room are perfectly vertical – but the corners are not at right-angles as they seem to be. The floor in the more distant left-hand corner, moreover, is actually at a lower level than the right-hand corner. Yet from a certain point of vantage the edges of this 'distortion room' are indistinguishable from those of a perfectly ordinary rectangular room of somewhat larger dimensions. The American psychologist Adelbert Ames was probably the first to make such a room, originally suggested by Helmholtz. Viewed through a single eye-hole (like the camera lens), the room provides no familiar binocular depth clues, and we find it hard to dissuade ourselves that it is anything but – well, an ordinary room. We become quite unable to compensate for the discrepancies in the apparent size of the people in the room. We are so inured to an environment of rectangular rooms that the distorted dimensions slip into the familiar pattern.

People who live in tribal cultures that do not favour straight lines and rectangles, like the Zulus with their domed round huts, succumb to these spatial illusions to a far lesser degree, if at all.

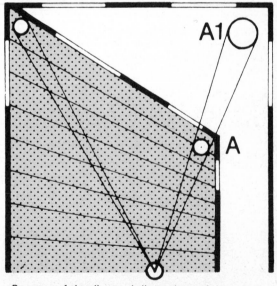

Because of the distorted dimensions of the room, we project the image of the person in corner A to position A1, where he seems far larger.

Behaviour Patterns

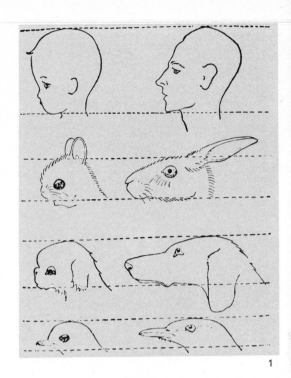

The ethologist Konrad Lorenz studied the range of stimuli that could elicit an inherited instinctive behaviour response. A goose, for example, will retrieve an egg that has rolled out of her nest. But the response occurs also with coloured cardboard Easter eggs and even plaster cylinders or cubes (Fig. 2). Apparently the object has only to have large surfaces and pass a 'hardness test' when the bird touches it with her beak. Innate responses play a role in man too, e.g. in our attitude towards babyhood (Fig. 1). A domed forehead, eyes low down in the head, fat cheeks and a toddling gait trigger the 'nursing instinct' in us, whether the stimulus emanates from a child, a baby animal or a doll or 'cuddly' toy. Doll-makers and comic-strip artists base their products on careful study of such responses.

1

2

Propaganda and advertising often shape our economic, political and religious views. Each year more than sixty million babies are born into the world's various indoctrination systems – hysterical adulation of trivial idols (Fig. 3) or intemperate hate of a synthetic 'enemy' (Fig. 4). What attitudes will such children strike when they grow up? With that prejudices will they view the world?

3

4

The Time Illusion

Only since the late eighteenth century have people worried about 'anachronisms' in painting and literature, showing things before their actual time, for it was then that they began to appreciate that every epoch has its own identity. A section from a painting (upper right) shows the High Priest Simeon, aged and with failing eyesight, with *oculos de vitro cum capsula* (eyes of glass in a frame) – but spectacles were invented only in the late thirteenth century. Columbus discovered America in 1492, evidently with the help of a telescope, according to a Caribbean stamp – but it was more than a hundred years later, in 1609, that Galileo improved the new Dutch invention to give a magnification of fifty rather than three.

> A rocket explorer named Wright
> Once traveled much faster than light.
> > He set out one day
> > In a relative way,
> And returned on the previous night.

Bifocal Trouble

The wise optician smiled and said:
'The upper half to look ahead;
The lower half whereby to read;
And thus one pair is all you need.
Have patience; in a week or two
Bifocals will not trouble you.'

I muttered as I left the shop:
'For distance vision use the top;
The bottom lenses you will need
When you sit down to write or read.'
I raised my right foot high in air
To mount a step which wasn't there.

The level street became a hill;
I looked at people standing still,
And, since I used the lower glass,
There seemed no room for me to pass.
I turned a corner of the street
And knocked a woman from her feet.

And all that day throughout the town
My eyes kept looking up and down,
'That fellow's drunk', I heard men say
As I went reeling down the way.
With those bifocals on my face
The town became a crazy place.

Bifocal troubles curious are:
The far seems near, the near seems far.
You step from heights that ne'er exist,
And jostle folks you should have missed;
Until man grows bifocal-wise
He finds he can't believe his eyes.

by Edgar A. Guest

When we look through a telescope, we look not only into deep space but into the remote past. We do not see the stars as they are but rather as they were aeons ago. We can never bring our picture of the firmament 'up to date'. The light that reaches us from Bellatrix in the constellation Orion started out 360 years ago, when Galileo and Kepler were plumbing the secrets of planetary orbits. For Daneb, in Cygnus, the period is 1,400 years, which takes us back to the fall of the Roman Empire. For Galaxy NGC 2362 it is 5,410 years, back to Sumer and Ur of the Chaldees; for the nebula in Andromeda 1·8 million light-years, the dawn of mankind; and for a galaxy in the Big Dipper we get 650 million light-years, back to the time when life first arose in the oceans.

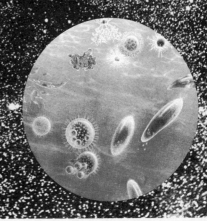

The Beginning and the End – How's That Again?

As long as anyone can remember, scholars and laymen have sought to calculate the age of the earth and when it will perish.

The most painstaking calculation was made by Bishop James Ussher of Ireland, who added up all the times given in the Bible and in 1654 came up with the pronouncement that the Lord had finished the work of Creation on Sunday, October 26, 4004 BC at nine o'clock in the morning.

No less painstaking were the calculations of Michael Stiftel, minister at Lochau in East Germany. He was convinced that the Scriptures concealed a secret code, and sought to decipher the Book of Revelation by substituting numerals for letters. In this way he obtained a total sum of 18,101,533 and in consequence proclaimed from his pulpit that Lochau, and with it the whole world, would end on 18 October, 1533. On the day the good people of Lochau waited until sunrise for their predicted end. When nine o'clock came round, they administered a sound thrashing to their minister.

'Then shall men and trees and rocks, big and little, be flung from the earth,' says this naïve medieval representation – but, alas, not when!

Antipodes? There Ain't No Such Thing!

In the third century AD the Church father Lactantius settled the problem of antipodes once and for all: 'Is there one so foolish as to believe in people whose feet point up and heads down? [See illustration at lower left.] Or that there be places where trees and bushes grow downwards and rain and hail fall upwards? They lie who so say.' In Zion, Illinois, Wilbur G. Voliva, head of the sect of Apostolic Catholics, reaffirmed in 1952, after having flown around the world several times, that 'the world is as flat as a saucer. There are no antipodes.'

Earth's Ultimate Incineration *from the* Physica Sacra *of the eighteenth-century Swiss naturalist Johann Jakob Scheuchzer.*

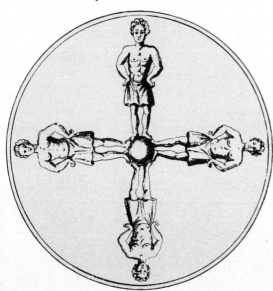

Speaking of Maps

Shapes of land masses differ considerably in different cartographic projection systems.

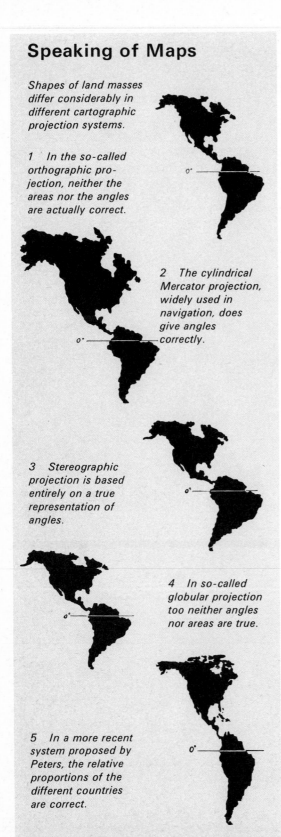

1   In the so-called orthographic projection, neither the areas nor the angles are actually correct.

2   The cylindrical Mercator projection, widely used in navigation, does give angles correctly.

3   Stereographic projection is based entirely on a true representation of angles.

4   In so-called globular projection too neither angles nor areas are true.

5   In a more recent system proposed by Peters, the relative proportions of the different countries are correct.

There is only one way of making a true representation of the earth, and that is the geographic globe. A spherical surface cannot be shown in two dimensions without distortion.

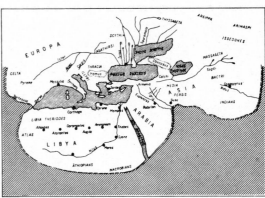

The terms 'longitude' and 'latitude' — derived from the Latin for 'length' and 'breadth' — seem illogical in the context of the Earth's sphere. In fact they date back to the Greek historian Herodotus (fifth century BC): because an east-west crossing of the Mediterranean took longer than the north-south voyage, he called the former dimension 'length' and the latter 'width'.

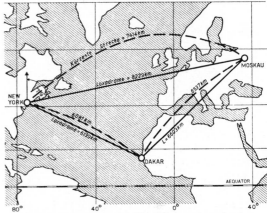

A straight line on the familiar Mercator projection is not the shortest distance between two points. The apparent straight-line triangle New York–Dakar–Moscow–New York measures 20,971 km, but the shortest route is shown by the dotted lines and is 939 km shorter!

Contour maps look realistic but often convey a false picture. Here the southern slopes are shown in shadow while the northern ones receive sunlight from high above in the north-west. Yet this 'wrong' representation accords with our visual habituation. When we turn the map upside-down, the valleys all bulge out into mountains. See also pp. 102–3.

When History Tells Fibs

The engraving above has latterly enjoyed unexampled popularity, being reproduced times without number for its purported representation of how medieval man burst the shell of ancient cosmogony. More than once it has been 'authoritatively' described as dating back to the early sixteenth century.

However charming and illuminating this picture may be, the fact is that it was commissioned for one of his books by the French astronomer Flammarion late in the nineteenth century. So much for *ex post facto* medieval 'authenticity'! As for the proverbial 'Egg of Columbus', which the great mariner is said to have stood upright on the table by causing the yolk to break inside the shell when no one else could make it stand on end, it can be traced back to the Renaissance architect Brunelleschi who designed the revolutionary Duomo in Florence. The engraving below allegedly shows him demonstrating the dome's feasibility with the help of an egg.

Like Trying to Keep Fleas in a Basket . . .

In a satirical seventeenth-century engraving on the use of chastity belts, Heinrich Schal concluded:

He who lock this cell / Must wear cap and bell, / A fool for all to tell, / Since others know full well / To ope the citadel / Cat's away, mice play.

Rather more than the locksmith's craft went into these guardians of virtue intended to forestall the temptations of lechery. More likely the lords and masters, when in their cups on their travels and absences, sought to outboast one another with tales of the fidelity of their spouses. Even so, the countless specimens that clutter so many museums are of doubtful authenticity, so far as actual use is concerned, for at an early date craft artisans discovered the erotic, not to say sadistic titillation elicited by these pseudo 'fences to dalliance', 'Venetian grilles' or 'Bergamese padlocks'.

Iron chastity belt in the Pachinger collection, Linz, Austria, sixteenth century.

Chastity belt of silver, sixteenth century.

Strange Things in the Sea and the Sky

La Mer poissons en abondance apporte,
Par dons divins que devons estimer.
Mais fort estrange est le Moyne de Mer,
Qui est ainsi que ce pourtrait le porte.

La terre n'a Evesques seulement,
Qui sont pour bulle en grand honneur et tiltre,
L'evesque croist en mer semblablement,
Ne parlant point, combien qu'il port Mitre.

This poem in archaic French appears in a curious book, *Omnium Fere Gentium*, which might be freely translated as 'about all the world's people'. It was published by Johannes Sluper in 1572. Many authors, it says, have written of strange creatures in the deep – mermaids, mer-monkeys, mer-Turks, mer-cows, mer-dogs, mer-horses – and people reading their accounts suffered nightmares.

From ancient times right down to modern Loch Ness, people have literally 'peopled' deep waters with strange creatures combining denizens of both land and sea. Though science has now 'exploded' many of the legends of the deep, a similar superstition, aided by technological imagination, has placed strange chariots in the sky. Scarcely a week passes by that does not bring reports of strange happenings in the 'Bermuda Triangle' of the Atlantic or of unexplained LITS (lights in the sky) or UFOs (unidentified flying objects, above, colour).

The Sphinxlike Sphinx

'Heathen priests were hidden inside the hollow head and made it seem as though the image were speaking to the people' – thus Johannes Helffrich noted in his diary in 1579, commenting on the huge and mysterious stone figure (below, left), half woman, half beast. Hewn from a huge rock, the creature inspired awe for millennia and remains to this day a symbol of inscrutability. In his African travel book, published in 1670, O. Dapper again represented the sphinx as a giant goddess (below, centre), and it was not until 1798 that Denon provided us with a more accurate rendering (below, right) – he recorded the wonders of the Nile as a member of Napoleon's great expedition. The Great Sphinx at Gizeh, fronting the Great Pyramid of the Pharaoh Chefren (above) was first dug out of the engulfing sand by Thutmosis IV of Egypt in 1420 BC. After the first garbled report in the West, it took some two hundred years before subjective impressions were replaced by objective accounts.

Garble-Garble – or How the Owl Became Something Else

Rumour, *by*
A. Paul Weber.

When someone copies another's drawing, the next person his, and so on, figures are stripped down to the geometry of familiar forms, enriched by the draughtsman's own wishful thoughts or unconsciously tailored to the supposed taste of the viewer. The bird drawing at left was the point of departure in a test in which successive renderings were passed along a line of twenty teenage students (upper twenty drawings on opposite page). The drawing that came out at the end was described as a 'barking dog'. The same test was tried on a group of book dealers at a German convention (fourteen drawings on lower part of opposite page). Major stages in the sequence were described as 'animal', 'face', 'hat', 'two objects'.

Ancient coins (below) were often copied in the early Celtic and Teutonic areas, and the counterfeits have been cited as evidence of the primitive pictorial traditions of these peoples. Actually, copying and recopying simply changed the face on the coins into the stereotyped form language of local cultures. The local craftsman merely selected those formal elements that were familiar to him.

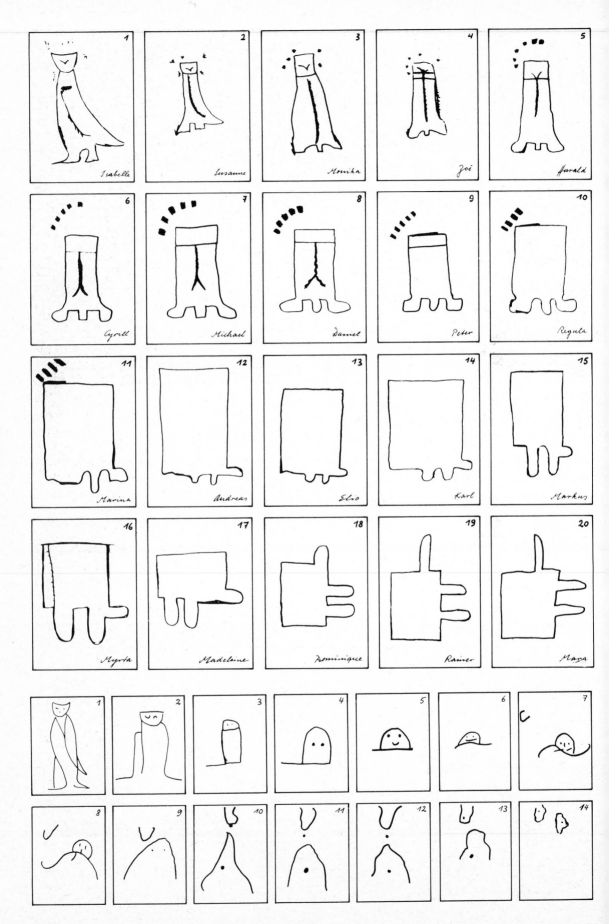

HOMO DILUVII TESTIS.

Bein - Gerüst
Eines in der
Sündflut ertrunkenen
Menschen.

Wir haben / nebst dem ohnfehlbaren Zeugnuß des Göttlichen Worts / so viel andere Zeugen jener allgemeinen und erschröcklichen Wasser-Flut ; als viel Länder / Stätte / Dörffer / Berge / Thäler / Stein-Brüche / Leim-Gruben sind. Pflanzen / Fische / vierfüssige Thiere / Ungiefer / Muscheln / Schnecken / ohne Zahl ; von Menschen aber / so domahls zu Grund gegangen / hat man biß dahin sehr wenig Uberbleibselen gefunden. Sie schwummen tod auf der obern Wasser-Fläche / und versaulten / und läßt sich von denen hin und wider befindlichen Gebeinen nicht allezeit schliessen / daß sie von Menschen seyen. Diese Bildnuß / welches in sauberem Holz-Schnitt der gelehrten und curiosen Welt zum Nachdenken vorlege / ist eines von sichersten ja ohnfehlbaren / Uberbleibselen der Sünd-Flut ; da finden sich nicht einige Lineament / auß welchen die reiche und fruchtbare Einbildung etwas / so dem Menschen gleichet / formieren kan / sondern eine gründliche Ubereinkunfft mit denen Theilen eines Menschlichen Bein-Gerüsts / ein vollkommenes Eben-Maß / ja selbs die in Stein (der auß dem Oningischen Stein-Bruch) eingesenkte Bein ; selbs auch welcher Theil sind in Natura übrig / und von übrigem Stein leicht zu unterscheiden. Dieser Mensch / dessen Grabmahl alle andere Römische und Griechische / auch Egyptische / oder andere Orientalische Monument an Alter und Gewühheit übertrifft / präsentiert sich von vornen. A B C ist der Umbfang des Stirn-Beins (alles in natürlicher Grösse) B. die Mitte der Stirn. A. das rechte Joch-Bein. C. das lincke. D E G H. die Augenleisten. K L die Dicke des Stirn-Beins / mit dessen beyden Tafelen / der äusseren und inneren. M. das Loch der unteren Augenleist / welches die Senn-Ader des fünfften Nerven hindurchläßt. N. Sind Reliquien von dem Gehirn / oder des harten Hirn-Häutleins. O. Die Gebein / welche die Augenleisten formiren. P. Die Siebförmigen und schwammichten Bein. P Q. Die Pflug-Schar / so durch die Mitte der Nasen hinunter gehet. U. Ein zimbliches Stuk vom vierten Backen-Bein. W. Scheinet seyn ein Stuk des Stirn-Muskuls. X. Uberbleibselen der Nasen. Y. Ein Stuk vom käuenden Muskul. B C. Ein Durchschnitt von dem untern Kiesel / wie der von dem dikeren Fortsatz gehet zu dem untern Ek oder Winkel. D. Stüfer vom untern Kienbaken gegen dem Kien. 1. 2. 3. &c. biß 16. sind 16. Rukgrat-Wirbel / nämlich 6. vom Hals / und 10. vom Ruken / da gemeinlich die Nebenfortsätze bloß ligen. E F. Ein Stuk vom Rabenförmigen Fortsaz des Schulter-Blatts. G H. Ein Stuk vom ersten Ripp / welches annoch mit Stein überzogen. i. Uberbleibselen von der Leber. Auß der ganzen Grösse läßt sich schliessen / in Gegenhalt der übrigen Theilen / daß die Höhe dieses Menschen steiget auf 58½. Pariser Zoll / welche entsprechen 5. Zürcher Schuhe 9⁷⁄₁₂. Decimal-Zoll.

Ex Musæo

Joh. Jacobi Scheuchzeri,
Med. D. Math. P.

Zürich zu finden bey

David Reding / Formschneider.

Im Jahr nach der Sündflut
MMMM XXXII.

PES PARISINUS.

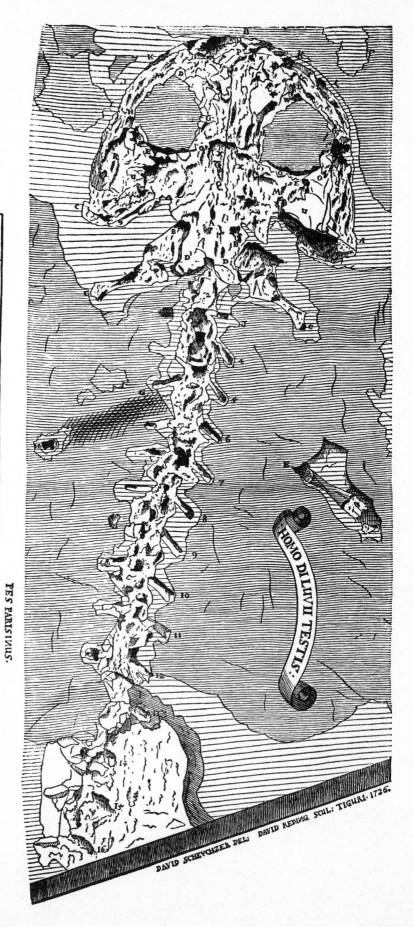

HOMO DILUVII TESTIS.

DAVID SCHEUCHZER DEL. DAVID REDING SCUL: TIGURI. 1726.

... a Questionable Shape

Local Smoke and Cinders

from *A Connecticut Yankee at King Arthur's Court* by Mark Twain

Sir Launceɪoɪ met up with old King Vgrivance of Ireland unexpectedly last weok over on the moor south of Sir Balmoral le Merveilleuse's hog dasture. The widow has been notified.

Expedition No. 3 will start adout the first of next▮mgnth▮on a search f8r Sir Sagramour le Desirous. It is in comand of the renowned Knight of the Red Lawns, assissted by Sir Persant of Inde, who is compete9t, intelligent, courteous, and in every ʌay a briⅽk, and furtʜer assisted by Sir Palamides the Saracen, who is no huckleberry himself. This is no pic-nic, these boys *m*ean busine&s.

The readers of the Hosannah will regret to learn that the hadndsome and popular Sir Charolais of Gaul, who during his four weeks' stay at the Bull and Halibut, this city, has won every heart by his polished manners and elegant cgnversation, will pᴜll out to-day for home. Give us another call, Charley!

The bdsiness end of the funeral of the late Sir Dalliance the duke's son of Cornwall, killed in an encounter with the Giant of the Knotted Bludgeon last ꞁuesday on the borders of the Plain of Enchantment was in the hands of the ever affable and əɥcient ▮Mumble, prince of un3ertakers, than whom there exists none by whom it were a more satisfying pleasure to have the last sad offices performed. Give him a trial.

The cordial thanks of the Hᴏsannah office are due, from editor down to devil, to the ever courteous and thoughtful Lord High Steward of the Palace's Thrid Assistant Valet for several saucaᵀs of ice crᴇam of a quality calculated to make the eyes of the recipients humid with gratitude; and it done it. When this ▮administration wants to chalk up a desirable na*m*e for early promotion, the Hosannah would like a chance to sudgest.

The Demoiselle Irene ꞇewlap, of South Astolat, is visiting her uncle, the popular host of the Cattlemen's Boarding Ho&se, Liver Lane, this city.

Skeleton of a giant salamander from the Far East, Andrias japonieus davidianus, *closest surviving relative of* Andrias scheuchzeri.

He That Seeketh Shall Find

The eminent Swiss naturalist Johann Jakob Scheuchzer dreamed of finding the one thing that would crown and complete his vast collection of rocks: fossil remains of man. Examining some calcareous slate from Öhningen on Lake Constance, he came upon a large skeleton which he at once recognized as the imprint of one of the countless bodies he thought the Deluge must have washed into his homeland. The find created a sensation because it was taken as proof of the reality of the Deluge.

There was no problem about dating the bones. The find was made in 1726, and Bible scholars had calculated that the Deluge took place in the year 2306 BC – *ergo* Noah's hapless contemporary had lain for 4032 years amid the rock strata.

The French biologist and geologist Georges Cuvier (1769–1832) recognized the bones as those of a giant salamander. With respect and Gallic wit, he named it *Andrias scheuchzeri*.

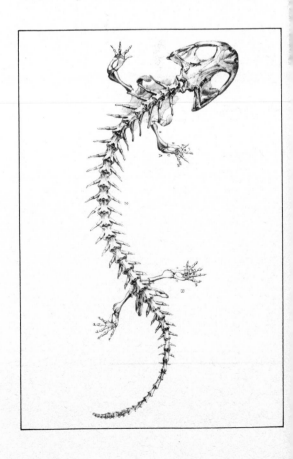

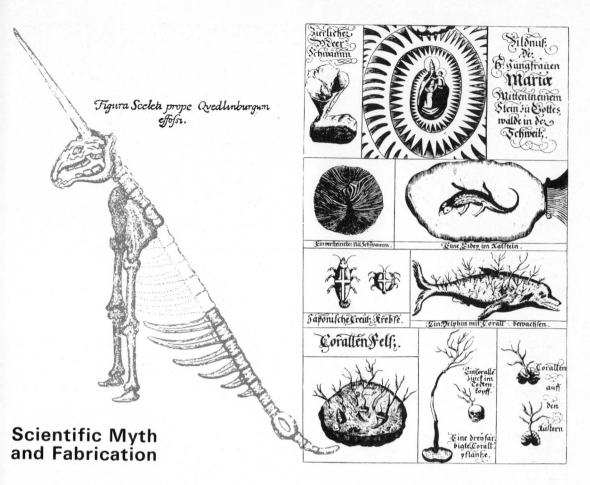

Figura Sceleti prope Qvedlinburgum effossi.

Scientific Myth and Fabrication

Adam Beringer, venerable Dean of the medical faculty of the University of Würzburg, Germany, marshalled all his scholarly resources in his *Lithographia Wirceburgensis* of 1726, in which he published his strange findings among the rocks. Besides genuine fossils, winged insects and plants, there were such figures as comets and even Hebrew and Arabic characters (below). The learned dean never suspected that spiteful pranksters among his colleagues

had slipped in artifacts among the real – until he found his own name on one of the rocks! Otto von Guericke reconstructed the mythical unicorn from fossil bones found near Quedlinburg, and Leibniz published a picture of it in his *Protogaea* of 1749 (upper left). Erasmus Franciscus found a miraculous petrified image of the Virgin, which he depicted with such other wonders as crustaceans 'from Japan' that bear a cross on their carapace (upper right).

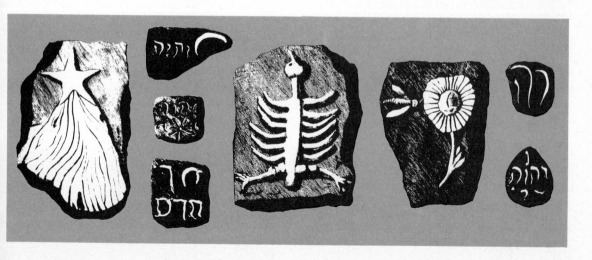

The Duck Tree

The idea of spontaneous generation survived from antiquity until comparatively recent times. Seemingly ineradicable, it held that life could arise from inanimate matter and even that plants might give birth to animals. Archelaus testified from Egypt that rotting spinal cord became transformed into serpents, that bees and wasps sprang from the cadavers of horses and oxen, that mites came from wax and scorpions from the flesh of crocodiles. Even Aristotle allowed eels and frogs to arise from mud. It would be tactless to enumerate all the eminent scientists who clung to a belief in spontaneous generation until after 1800.

The most interesting among plants thought to bring forth animals is the Duck Tree (upper right). In his work on

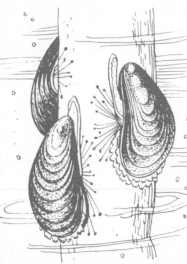

birds, fish and beasts, Leonhard Baldner wrote: 'In the year of our Lord 1649, the 27th of February, I owned of such tree geese twain. This bird is a stranger to us, hence beareth the name of tree goose. The learned Dr Gesner sayeth the tree that bringeth forth such fruit groweth in Scotland. The fruit hath the shape of an worm, folded up together into a leaf, and when it falleth into the water betimes, the breath of life doth arise within it and it formeth itself into a gosling, sprouteth feathers and taketh wing.'

This quaint sylvan fruit is none other than the ring-necked goose, *Branta vernicla*, which used to be popularly called 'barnacle goose'. As for the so-called duck tree, it is associated with a species of barnacle, *Lepas anatifera*, related to the crustaceans, which is found attached to driftwood (upper left). *Homunculus*, diminutive man, also flourished in the scientific imagination once spermatozoa (literally sperm animals) had been discovered by the Dutch naturalist Anthony van Leeuwenhoek in the seventeenth century. Contemporary microscopists thought they saw what they wanted to see through their crude lenses – tiny little figures in the sperm heads.

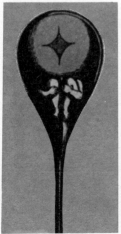

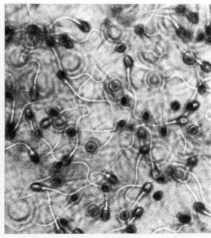

by speech or writing or answers appear to most of his hearers to be wholly ignorant of the subjects about which he is attempting to write or speak; for they are ignorant sometimes of the fact that it is not the soul of the writer or speaker that is being convicted but the nature of each of the four, which is essentially defective. But it is the methodical study of all these stages, passing in turn from one to another, up and down, which with difficulty implants knowledge, when the man himself, like his object, is of a fine nature; but if his nature is bad – and, in fact, the condition of most men's souls in respect of learning and of what are termed 'morals' is either naturally bad or else corrupted – then not even Lynceus himself could make such folk see. In one word, neither receptivity nor memory will ever produce knowledge in him who has no affinity with the object, since it does not germinate to start with in alien states of mind; consequently neither those who have no natural connection or affinity with things just, and all else that is fair, although they are both receptive and retentive in various ways of other things, nor yet those who possess such affinity but are unreceptive and unretentive – none, I say, of these will ever learn to the utmost possible extent the truth of virtue nor

Wheel shape enclosing a sun worshipper: detail from a lintel and enclosure of a Buddhist stupa in Barhut, second century BC.

yet of vice. For in learning these objects it is necessary to learn at the same time both what is false and what is true of the whole of existence, and that through the most diligent and prolonged investi-

gation, as I said at the commencement; and it is by means of the examination of each of these objects, comparing one with another – names and definitions, visions and sense-perceptions – proving them by kindly proofs and employing questionings and answerings that are void of envy – it is by such means, and hardly so, that there bursts out the light of

A spider in her spoked web.

intelligence and reason regarding each object in the mind of him who uses every effort of which mankind is capable. And this is the reason why every serious man in dealing with really serious subjects carefully avoids writing, lest thereby he may possibly cast them as a prey to the envy and stupidity of the public. In one word, then, our conclusion must be that whenever one sees a man's written compositions – whether they be the laws of a legislator or anything else in any other form – these are not his most serious works, if so be that the writer himself be serious: rather those works abide in the fairest region he possesses. If, however, these really are his serious efforts, and put into writing, it is not 'the gods' but mortal men who 'Then of a truth themselves have utterly ruined his senses. . . .'

Translation by R. G. Bury

The Circle

Plato, Epistle VII

Every existing object has three things which are the necessary means by which knowledge of that object is acquired; and the knowledge itself is a fourth thing; and as a fifth one must postulate the object itself which is cognizable and true. First of these comes the name; secondly the definition; thirdly the image; fourthly the knowledge. If you wish, then, to understand what I am now saying, take a single example and learn from it what applies to all.

There is an object called a circle, which has for its *name* the word we have just mentioned; and secondly, it has a *definition*, composed of names and verbs; for 'that which is everywhere equidistant from the extremities to the centre' will be the definition of that object which has for its name 'round' and 'spherical' and 'circle'. And in the third place there is that object which is in course of being portrayed and obliterated, or of being shaped with a lathe, and falling into decay; but none of these affections is suffered by the circle itself, whereto all these others are related inasmuch as it is distinct therefrom.

Fourth comes *knowledge* and intelligence and true opinion regarding these objects; and these we must assume to form a single whole, which does not exist in vocal utterance or in bodily forms but in souls; whereby it is plain that it differs both from the nature of the circle itself and from the three previously mentioned. And of these four intelligence approaches most nearly in kinship and similarity to the fifth, and the rest are farther removed.

The same is true alike of the straight and of the spherical form, and of colour, and of the good and the fair and the just, and of all bodies whether manufactured or naturally produced (such as fire and water and all such substances), and of all living creatures, and of all moral actions or passions in souls. For unless a man somehow or other grasps the four of these, he will never perfectly acquire knowledge of the fifth, moreover, these four attempt to express the quality of each object no less than its real essence, owing to the weakness inherent in language; and for this reason, no man of intelligence will ever venture to commit to it the concepts of his reason, especially when it is unalterable – as is the case with what is formulated in writing.

But here again you must learn further the meaning of this last statement. Every one of the circles which are drawn in geometric exercises or are turned by the lathe is full of what is opposite to the fifth, since it is in contact with the straight everywhere; whereas the circle itself, as we affirm, contains within itself no share greater or less of the opposite nature. And none of the objects, we affirm, has any fixed name, nor is there anything to prevent forms which are now called 'round' from being called 'straight', and the 'straight' 'round'. And men will find the names no less firmly fixed when they have shifted them and apply them in an opposite sense. Moreover, the same account

Time exposure of the night sky, aimed at the celestial pole.

holds good of the definition, also, that, inasmuch as it is compounded of names and verbs, it has no case fixed with sufficient firmness. And so with each of the four, their inaccuracy is an endless topic; but, as we mentioned a moment ago, the main point is this, that while there are two separate things, the real essence and the quality, and the soul seeks to know not the quality but the essence, each of the four proffers to the soul either in word or in concrete form that which is not sought; and by thus causing each object which is described or exhibited to be always easy of refutation by the senses, it fills practically all men with all manner of perplexity and uncertainty. In respect, however, of those other objects the truth of which, owing to our bad training, we usually do not so much as seek – being content with such of the images as are proffered – those of us who answer are not made to look ridiculous by those who question, we being capable of analysing and convicting the four. But in all cases where we compel a man to give the fifth as his answer and to explain it, anyone who is able and willing to upset the argument gains the day, and makes the person who is expounding his view

The Maid of Orléans

Jeanne d'Arc, born in 1412 in Domrémy, persuaded the timid Dauphin to entrust her with a small army to lift the English siege of Orléans. Her warriors expelled the English forces from the Loire area, which made it possible for the Dauphin to be anointed and crowned king in Reims. Captured by the Burgundians, Jeanne was delivered to the English in return for 10,000 *livres*. In 1431 an ecclesiastical court found her guilty of heresy and sentenced her to be burned at the stake, a verdict that was quashed some twenty years later.

The transcript of her trial gathered dust in government archives down to the early nineteenth century, no one having felt any particular need of a virginal heroine. But when war with Britain seemed to impend, Napoleon unearthed the legendary figure and the church fostered the myth as an antidote to atheism, which was then flourishing.

Jeanne d'Arc was canonized after the First World War at a cost to the French Exchequer of 30 million gold francs and the resumption of French diplomatic relations with the Holy See, suspended since the Revolution.

There could have been no burning at the stake in 1431, since the sentence passed by the ecclesiastical court was never confirmed by the secular judiciary; this would have been necessary before the sentence could be carried out. Indeed, according to some sources Jeanne turned up again five years after her 'cremation', on 20 May 1436, in St Privey, and was subsequently given a triumphal reception by the people of Orléans. Early in October 1436 she surrendered her virginity to a nobleman from Lorraine, Robert des Armoises, and went to live at Château Jaulney, where she died in 1449. The château is still in existence.

On the 500th anniversary of her 'burning', 29 May 1931, Jeanne was elected patron saint of the French army; and Charles de Gaulle strongly resisted any imputations that the virginal national idol had died in a connubial bed. Literature, art and the cinema have spun out the legend into a wishful dream that makes a far stronger appeal to the imagination than the sober facts of history. The entire documentation, including the forgotten records of the ecclesiastical commission of inquiry in Poitiers, now lies in the Vatican. The late church historian Edouard Schneider remarked: 'The exalted authorities are reluctant to kill the legend.'

The Bastille

The French celebrate 14 July, the anniversary of the storming of the Bastille, as their national holiday. The original event, in 1789, ushered in the Revolution. The grim fortress, so runs the story, had inspired fear and terror among the people of Paris for centuries, and when the enraged crowd stormed its walls, a dreadful bloodbath ensued.

Actually, the Bastille was a kind of feudal prison, rather as pictured in the Strauss operetta *Die Fledermaus*. It had originally been a castle and was turned into a place of detention only under Henri IV. According to Frantz Funck-Brentano's *Légendes et Archives de la Bastille* (1898), the realities differed markedly from the imaginative atrocity stories. The inmates lived in comfortable circumstances as 'guests of the king' and were even permitted to have their own servants and furnishings during their involuntary sojourn. The evil reputation of the place was largely a product of the sensational press of the time, which occasionally distorted and inflated resentful reports from prisoners of high social status. The guards of the Bastille were disabled or retired soldiers, augmented by a platoon of Swiss mercenaries.

A riot did, of course, take place on 14 July. The main instigators seem to have been a group of hooligans who invaded the building and liberated seven inmates – four forgers, a libertine who had been committed by his family, and two madmen who were admitted to the asylum at Charenton on the following day. As for the 'massacre', it was perpetrated by a riot-inflamed kitchen boy who cut off the head of Governor de Launay and paraded it on a pikestaff through the streets of Paris at the head of a screaming mob.

A group of juveniles took part in stripping the prison vaults of ancient bric-à-brac. A medieval suit of armour the naïve pilferers took to be a torture device, and they thought that an obsolete printing press was a rack. The 'liberators' carried this 'torture chamber equipment' out into the daylight. By the time news of the Bastille caper reached the French provinces, it had become so grossly embellished and magnified that it would have been a downright pity not to have commemorated the event as a national holiday.

William Tell, standing before the cruel steward, aims at an apple on the head of his son. Actually, it was the steward who was named Tell, or rather Tillendorf, while the crossbowman was probably Rudolf Stauffacher.

What's in a Name?

Would Hitler have become dictator, if his illegitimately born father had kept the faintly ludicrous name of Schickelgruber? Would Cary Grant have become a film idol under his original name of Archie Leach, or Garbo a legend as Greta Gustafsson? Names are sometimes changed for political reasons: during the First World War the House of Hanover became the House of Windsor, the Battenbergs the Mountbattens. *Sauerkraut* was rechristened 'liberty cabbage' in America. Hamburgers are virtually unknown in Hamburg and frankfurters in Frankfurt, except as American re-imports. In Britain the bun Americans call an 'English muffin' is known as a scone (pronounced *scon*). And an American shopping for 'thumb tacks' in London would draw blank stares at stationery shops, where they are known as 'drawing pins'. Often nicknames take the place of real names. Few people will recognize Theotocopoulos, Fiesole, and Robusti as famous painters, but many know El Greco, Fra Angelico and Tintoretto. Is a name an arbitrary convention, a symbol, or the real thing or person, fixed for all time? Whatever the answer, great power may reside in a name. The Hebrew name of the Almighty, Jehovah or Yahwe, could not even be spoken.

> And the best and the worst of this is
> That neither is most to blame,
> If you have forgotten my kisses
> And I have forgotten your name.
>
> SWINBURNE

136

Baron Münchhausen

after Gottfried Bürger

Imagine my predicament, gentlemen! Behind me a lion, before me a crocodile, on my left a raging torrent, on my right an abyss, infested, as I learned afterward, by venomous serpents.

Such a plight might have stunned even a Hercules, and indeed, I fell senseless to the ground. My last conscious expectation was that at any moment I should feel the teeth and claws of the enraged cat or be engulfed in the reptile's gaping jaws. But within seconds I heard a loud and unfamiliar sound. At last I dared raise my head and cast about; and what do you think, to my inexpressible joy I discovered that the lion had apparently leaped – at the very moment when I sank down – straight into the crocodile's maw. His head was buried in the monster's throat, and both creatures were trying with might and main to disengage. Just in time I leaped to my feet, drew my hunting-knife and hacked off the lion's head at one blow, the body falling twitching at my feet. With the stock of my rifle I rammed the severed head even deeper into the crocodile's throat, causing the beast to choke to death.

Soon after this full victory over two terrible adversaries, my friend returned to learn why I had lagged behind. After we had congratulated each other, we measured the crocodile and found it to be in length forty feet and seven inches, Paris measure.

No sooner had we related this extraordinary adventure to the Governor than he dispatched a wagon with several men to retrieve the carcases of the two beasts. Nothing would do but that a local tanner must work the lion's pelt into a number of tobacco pouches, some of which I presented to several of my acquaintances in Ceylon. On my return to Holland, I presented the remaining ones to the burgomasters who wished to reciprocate with a gift of a thousand ducats, which I had considerable difficulty in refusing.

The skin of the crocodile was stuffed by a taxidermist in the usual way, and it now constitutes one of the greatest curiosities in the Amsterdam museum, where the guide is eager to retell the story to anyone who wishes to hear it, adding some embellishments, which depart considerably from truth and probability. He is fond of saying, for example, that the lion leaped clear through the crocodile and was about to escape by the back-door, so to speak, when Monsieur the famous Baron (as he was wont to call me) hacked its head off and with it some three feet of the crocodile's tail. 'The crocodile', the caitiff often goes on, 'was far from indifferent to the loss of his tail, whipped about and snatched away Monsieur's hunting-knife, which he wolfed down with such avidity that it tore straight into his heart, whereupon he fell dead.'

I need scarcely tell you, gentlemen, of my embarrassment over this rapscallion's impudent lies. People who do not know me may well, in this sceptical age, be induced by this prevarication to distrust the truth of my real adventures, a reaction quite properly resented by any man of honour.

Gottfried Bürger's pleasantly preposterous Baron Münchhausen, who lived so much in his fantasy world that he came to confound illusion and reality, believing the tall stories he told.

Footprints in the Sand of Time

Alexander Dubček was a popular hero during the 'Prague Spring', but after the Soviet tanks moved in he became an Orwellian 'unperson'. He had to disappear even from documentary photographs commemorating great occasions. In the picture above he is shown with President Svoboda. In the picture below, the image of Svoboda was enlarged, while the man who worked for 'Communism with a human face' simply vanished. In the process, the house in the background lost a chimney, and the hard-pressed retoucher forgot to eliminate Dubček's right foot, which remains as the sole faint reminder that here once stood a brave man.

The Invisible Men

In 1920, the Second Congress of the Communist International assembled the party élite in Moscow (picture below). Most of the delegates never dreamed that some day they would become 'unpersons' and vanish before the retoucher's magic brush – Radek, left, with cigarette; Nikolai Bukharin (whom Lenin in his will called the 'darling of the party') on Radek's left; Grigori Zinoviev, on Gorki's left; even Gorki's son Peshkov, with hat, behind Gorki. In the re-written history of the Soviet Union, only Lenin and Gorki remain (left). Most of the 'retouchees' perished during the Great Purges of the late 30s.

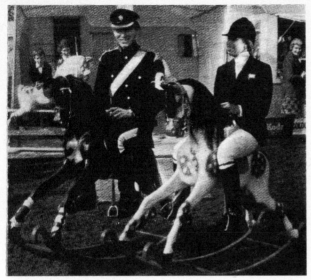

Rocking Them on Their Heels

Tall in the Saddle

Hopalong Anne

The Princess and the Pony

Mark, When Are You Going to Give Me a Hunter?

Backing the Wrong Horse

Captions such as those above accompanied pictures of Princess Anne on a rocking-horse that passed through the German press shortly after her engagement was announced. This all-too-familiar sensation-mongering is often the product of scissors and paste-pot rather than honest reporting.

The picture at the top appeared in the German colour magazine *Bunte Illustrierte*, which regaled its readers with the epochal news that Princess Anne and her fiancé Mark Phillips were rocking and galloping towards matrimony.

To give priority its due, another shot from what was evidently a series had already graced – if that is the right word – the front page of *Paris-Match* (centre). The French editors, however, were at least honest enough to hide away a note in small print admitting that they had stripped in Princess Anne's face over that of an unknown girl who had posed with the then Lieutenant Phillips for a day.

In the picture at the bottom we get to the bottom of the hoax. Syndicated by Camera Press, it shows the girl who had to sacrifice her head to the gossip columns. She is Mary Gordon Watson, who has ridden with the handsome officer more than once.

I Saw a Blazing Comet Drop Down Hail . . .

Many traditional children's rhymes and riddles rely for their effect on illusion: the punning play on words, the confusion induced by an absence of punctuation, the straightforward question wreathed in complicated irrelevances, or the perplexing nature of everyday objects described in unfamiliar terms. Many such rhymes have been popular for hundreds of years; equivalent versions can be found in other European languages, and some are recorded in Greek and Latin.

White bird featherless
Flew from Paradise,
Pitched on the castle wall;
Along came Lord Landless,
Took it up handless,
And rode away horseless to the King's white hall.

SOLUTION: the snow and the sun.

Make three-fourths of a cross,
And a circle complete,
And let two semi-circles
On a perpendicular meet;
Next add a triangle
That stands on two feet;
Next two semi-circles
And a circle complete.

SOLUTION: T–O–B–A–C–C–O.

In marble halls as white as milk,
Lined with a skin as soft as silk,
Within a fountain crystal-clear,
A golden apple doth appear.
No doors there are to this stronghold,
Yet thieves break in and steal the gold.

SOLUTION: an egg.

I saw a peacock with a fiery tail
I saw a blazing comet drop down hail
I saw a cloud with ivy circled round
I saw a sturdy oak creep on the ground
I saw a pismire swallow up a whale
I saw a raging sea brim full of ale
I saw a Venice glass sixteen foot deep
I saw a well full of men's tears that weep
I saw their eyes all in a flame of fire
I saw a house as big as the moon and higher
I saw the sun even in the midst of night
I saw the man that saw this wondrous sight.

As I was going to St Ives,
I met a man with seven wives,
Each wife had seven sacks,
Each sack had seven cats,
Each cat had seven kits:
Kits, cats, sacks, and wives,
How many were there going to St Ives?

SOLUTION: one.

Two legs sat upon three legs
With one leg in his lap;
In comes four legs
And runs away with one leg;
Up jumps two legs,
Catches up three legs,
Throws it after four legs,
And makes him bring back one leg.

SOLUTION: a man sits on a three-legged stool with a leg of mutton in his lap. A dog snatches the mutton and runs away with it. The man jumps up and throws the stool at the dog, who brings back the leg of mutton.

I need not your needles, they're needless to me,
For kneading of needles were needless, you see;
But did my neat trousers but need to be kneed,
I then should have need of your needles indeed.

*Nasticreechia
Krorluppia*

*Piggiwiggia
Pyramidalis*

From Edward Lear's Nonsense Botany *(1871).*

The Emperor's New Clothes

by Hans Christian Andersen

Many years ago there lived an Emperor who was so fond of new clothes that he spent all his money on them in order to be beautifully dressed. . . . In the great city in which he lived there was always something going on; every day many strangers came there. One day two impostors arrived who gave themselves out as weavers, and said that they knew how to manufacture the most beautiful cloth imaginable. Not only were the texture and pattern uncommonly beautiful, but the clothes which were made of the stuff possessed this wonderful property that they were invisible to anyone who was not fit for his office, or who was unpardonably stupid.

'Those must indeed be splendid clothes,' thought the Emperor. 'If I had them on I could find out which men in my kingdom are unfit for the offices they hold; I could distinguish the wise from the stupid! Yes, this cloth must be woven for me at once.' And he gave both the impostors much money, so that they might begin their work.

They set up two weaving-looms, and began to act as if they were working, but they had not the least thing on the looms. They also demanded the finest silk and the best gold, which they put in their pockets. . . . Everybody in the town was talking of the magnificent cloth. Now the Emperor wanted to see it himself while it was still on the loom. With a great crowd of select followers . . . he went to the cunning impostors. . . .

'Is it not splendid!' said the statesmen. 'See, your Majesty, what a texture! What colours!' And then they pointed to the empty loom, for they believed that the others could see the cloth quite well.

'What!' thought the Emperor, 'I can see nothing! This is indeed horrible! Am I stupid? Am I not fit to be Emperor? That would be the most dreadful thing that could happen to me. 'Oh, it is very beautiful,' he said. 'It has my gracious approval!' . . . His whole Court round him looked and looked, and saw not more than the others; but they said like the Emperor, 'Oh, it is beautiful!' And they advised him to wear these new and magnificent clothes for the first time at the great procession which was soon to take place. . . .

Throughout the whole of the night before the morning on which the procession was to take place, the impostors were up and working by the light of sixteen candles. The people could see that they were very busy making the Emperor's new clothes ready. They pretended they were taking the cloth from the loom, cut with huge scissors in the air, sewed with needles without thread, and then said at last, 'Now the clothes are finished!' . . .

'Will it please your gracious Majesty to take off your clothes,' said the impostors, 'then we will put on the new clothes, here before the mirror.'

The Emperor took off all his clothes, and the impostors placed themselves before him as if they were putting on each part of his new clothes which was ready, and the Emperor turned and bent himself in front of the mirror. . . .

'Look, I am ready,' said the Emperor. 'Doesn't it sit well!' And he turned himself again to the mirror to see if his finery was on all right. The chamberlains who were used to carry the train put their hands near

the floor as if they were lifting up the train; then they acted as if they were holding something in the air. They would not have it noticed that they could see nothing.

So the Emperor went along in the procession under the splendid canopy, and all the people in the streets and at the windows said, 'How matchless are the Emperor's new clothes! That train fastened to his robe, how beautifully it hangs!' None of the Emperor's clothes had met with such approval as these had.

'But he has nothing on!' said a little child at last. 'Listen to the voice of innocence!' said the father, and each one whispered to his neighbour what the child had said.

'But he has nothing on!' cried out all the people at last. This struck the Emperor, for it seemed to him as if they were right; but he thought to himself, 'I must go on with the procession now.' And the chamberlains walked along still more uprightly, holding up the train which was not there at all.

A Real Turkey – or Rather a Wrong One

The picture above shows a detail from what is purported to be an early Gothic church fresco painting. Professor Alfred Stange, an art historian, offered this comment in 1940: 'Painted around 1280, the work shows the painter to have been remarkably observant in depicting even the tiniest characteristic with complete verisimilitude.'

In another case, the recovery of splendid wall paintings in the Church of St Mary in Lübeck, Germany, was the occasion for a commemorative issue of charity postage stamps. Hans Jürgen Hausen, another art historian, commented: 'Until they were rediscovered in 1942 . . . these murals had been hidden for almost 500 years beneath coats of whitewash.'

The trouble with these expert opinions is that (a) the turkey was introduced from South America to the English Court only in 1524 and (b) the early Gothic master was unmasked as one Lothar Malskat, born on 3 May 1913 in Königsberg in what was then East Prussia.

Imaginative forgery is one of the most intelligent and creative forms of deception.

Illusion and Anti-Illusion in the Theatre

Illusionism in the theatre was at its height from about 1750 to 1910, when the aim was to create the maximum illusion of reality on the stage, both in the set and by means of stage machinery, where considerable ingenuity was often employed (Figs 2, 3).

When Karl Friedrich Schinkel, the distinguished German architect, designed the setting for Schiller's *Die Jungfrau von Orleans* in 1817, 'one of the most felicitous ideas was undoubtedly that of allowing the spectators, during Joan of Arc's magnificent monologue, to see a part of the city and cathedral of Rheims. . . .' (Fig. 1).

By the 1920s a reaction had set in, and an 'anti-illusionistic' theatre developed which underlined the unreality of the stage, delighting in the artificiality of the performance. A prime example is the work of Bertolt Brecht (Fig. 4), who aimed to force the spectator into objective consideration of the social problems depicted in his plays.

1

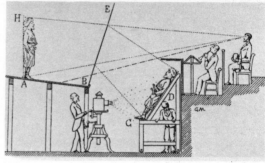

3

1 *Schinkel,* Die Jungfrau von Orleans, *Berlin 1817: view painted from precise sketches.*
2 *Daumier, human wave machine.*
3 *'Pepper's ghost', a technique invented in the 1860s: a sheet of plain glass was set up between the audience and the stage, and on it was seen the reflection of the actor beneath the stage.*
4 *A 1931 production of* Man is Man, *by Brecht.*

2

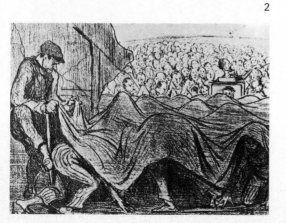

4

'Like Two Servants, Supporting an Elderly Gentleman' – The Elusive Rings of Saturn

The discovery and elucidation of the rings of the planet Saturn provide a fine example of how illusion and obfuscation can supplement each other in science. Saturn had been known from olden times, but it was only with the invention of the telescope that its unique configuration became evident. Galileo was the first to see it. In 1610 he wrote to Kepler that he had made an important discovery for which he wished to claim priority and which he had embodied in the following anagram:

SMAISMRMILMEPOETALEVMIBUNENUGTTAVIRAS

It was perhaps not the question of priority alone that preoccupied Galileo, but the possibility of ridicule that so often greeted unprecedented discoveries, and, more seriously, of possible sanctions in reprisal for anything that ran counter to established doctrine. However that may have been, Galileo confided the solution to his anagram a bit later to Giuliano de' Medici, ambassador of Tuscany in Prague. It was: *Altissimam planetam tergeminum observavi* – Latin for 'I have observed the uppermost [outermost] planet threefold.' Galileo, in other words, had seen the small disc of Saturn flanked on either side by two smaller protuberances or spheres, 'like two servants', as he put it, 'supporting an elderly gentleman'. Two years later Galileo was amazed to note that these two *ansae* (Latin for handles), as they came to be called, had vanished without a trace!

Protuberances, flanking spheres, handles – these seem a long way from what we know today as the still mysterious flat rings of Saturn, inclined at an angle of 27° to the planet's orbital plane; but we must remember that the human brain, confronted with a sense impression without precedent, naturally tends to assimilate it to something within its experience. The drawings on this page show what various astronomers, beginning with Galileo, thought they saw. As to the mysterious disappearance, well, even today, through powerful telescopes, it is not easy to make out the rings when they are seen edge-on.

It was the great Dutch astronomer Christiaan Huygens who, after a false start in 1656 (see diagram), finally solved the puzzle and saw the 'handles' as the flat rings they are; but almost half a century after Galileo, Huygens still cautiously chose a Latin anagram as the vehicle for his discovery. His, however, ran alphabetically, as follows:

AAAAAAA CCCCC D EEEEE G H IIIIIII LLLL MM NNNNNNNNN OOOO PP Q RR S TTTT UUUUU

Properly assembled, this yields *annulo cingitur, tenui plano, nusquam cohaerente, ad ecliptam inclinatio*, or 'surrounded by a thin, flat ring that nowhere touches and is inclined to the ecliptic'.

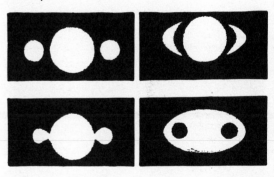

This is what five astronomers thought they saw upon first observing the planet Saturn through a telescope.

This is the solution to the baffling problem of the appearance of Saturn which Huygens published in 1659. He met the inevitable objections by predicting when the ring would again become 'invisible'. It was only in 1675 that the astronomer Cassini established the existence of not just one but of two concentric rings of Saturn.

The Dream of Pygmalion

Pygmalion, king of Cyprus, carved an image of Aphrodite in ivory and fell in love with it. Answering his pleas, the goddess brought the statue to life. Perhaps the wishful dream behind this legend underlies all art. The illusion of beauty changes from age to age, from the naïve ideal of Aurignacian man to the idealized vulgarity of Barbarella, who besots the galaxy. Plato posited 'the fair' as an absolute, but David Hume, the Scottish philosopher, maintained that 'Beauty in things exists in the mind which contemplates them.' Perhaps beauty simply reflects what people of a certain time and place feel to be beautiful. Plutarch put it in a nutshell: 'The Persians favour hooknosed men and believe them to be the fairest, for Cyrus, most beloved of their kings, possessed such a nose.'

Left to right:
The Venus of Willendorf, Paleolithic age, c. *30,000 BC.*

The fertility goddess Ishtar, Sumerian–Accadian, c. *2000 BC.*

Venus Genetrix, by Callimachus, fifth century BC.

The Birth of Venus, by Botticelli, fifteenth century *AD.*

Comic-strip character Barbarella, twentieth century.

that whatever it is that is distorting our vision, it must emanate from the pear tree. For nothing in the world would have dissuaded me from believing that you had lain here carnally with your lady, until I heard you claiming that I had apparently been doing something which I most certainly never did, nor even thought of doing for a moment.' At this point he was interrupted by the lady, who rose to her feet and said to her husband, in tones of considerable annoyance: 'The devil take you if you have such a low opinion of me as to suppose that, had I wanted to comport myself as scandalously as you claim to have seen, I should do it before your very eyes. You may rest assured that if I should ever feel the urge to do it, I should not do so out here in the garden. On the contrary, I would find myself a nice comfortable bed, and arrange the whole thing so discreetly that if you ever got to know about it I should be very much surprised.' Nicostratus now felt that they must both be speaking the truth, and that they could never have brought themselves to do such a thing in his presence. So he ceased his shouting and raving, and began to talk about the strangeness of the thing, and about the miraculous way in which a man's eyesight could be affected by climbing a tree.

Vision Reversed

The Ninth Tale of the Seventh Day,
The Decameron, by Boccaccio

Albeit Lydia could scarcely wait for Pyrrhus to take her in his arms, she was determined to keep the promise she had given him. She therefore pretended to be ill, and one day, when Nicostratus came to visit her after breakfast, attended only by Pyrrhus, she asked him whether they would help her down to the garden so as to relieve the tedium of her sick-bed. So they conveyed her to the garden, Nicostratus supporting her on one side and Pyrrhus on the other, and set her down on a lawn at the foot of a beautiful pear tree. And after sitting there together for a while, she turned to Pyrrhus, to whom she had sent word beforehand of what he was to do, and said: 'Pyrrhus, I long to have one or two of those pears. Climb the tree and throw some of them down.' Pyrrhus, having swiftly clambered up, began to throw down some of the pears, and as he was doing so, he called out to Nicostratus, saying: 'For shame, sir, what are you doing? And you, my lady, how can you be so brazen as to allow it in my presence? Do you think I am blind? Until a moment ago you were very ill; how can you have recovered so rapidly? If you wanted to indulge in that sort of thing, you have plenty of fine bedrooms in the house – why do you not go and do it in one of those? It would surely be more seemly than doing it here in my presence.' The lady turned to her husband and said: 'What's Pyrrhus talking about? Is he quite mad?' Whereupon Pyrrhus said: 'I am not mad, my lady. Do you think I cannot see you?' Nicostratus gaped at him in blank astonishment, and said: 'Why, Pyrrhus, I think you must be dreaming.' 'No my lord,' he replied, 'I am wide awake, and so are you, it appears. In fact, you are putting so much vigour into it that if this tree were to be given so hard a buffeting, there would not be a single pear left on it.' 'What can this mean?' said the lady. 'Can he really be seeing what he professes to be seeing? Heaven help me, if only I were fit and strong, I should climb up there

and see for myself what these marvels are that he claims to be witnessing.' Meanwhile, Pyrrhus continued to pour forth a stream of similar remarks from his vantage-point in the pear tree, until eventually Nicostratus ordered him to come down. And when he had reached the ground, Nicostratus said: 'What is it you claim to be seeing?' 'I do believe,' said Pyrrhus, 'that you take me for an idiot or a lunatic. Since you force me to speak, I saw you lying on top of your lady, and as soon as I started to descend, you got up and sat in the spot where you are now sitting.' To which Nicostratus replied: 'You are certainly behaving like an idiot, for we have not moved in the slightest since you climbed up the tree.' 'What is the use of arguing about it?' said Pyrrhus. 'I can only repeat that I saw you, and you were going to it merrily.' Nicostratus grew visibly more astonished, until finally he said: 'I am going to find out for myself whether this pear tree is enchanted, and what kind of marvels you can see from its branches.' So up he climbed, and no sooner had he done so than Pyrrhus and his lady began to make love together, whereupon Nicostratus, seeing what they were about, shouted: 'Ah, vile strumpet, what are you doing? And you, Pyrrhus, after all the trust I placed in you!' And so saying, he began to climb down again. 'We are just sitting here quietly,' said Pyrrhus and the lady. But on seeing him descending, they returned to their former places. No sooner had Nicostratus descended and found them sitting where he had left them than he began to shower them with abuse. 'Why, Nicostratus,' said Pyrrhus, 'I must confess that you were right after all, and that my eyes were deceiving me when I was up in the tree. My only reason for saying this is that I know for a fact that you too have had a similar illusion. If you think I am wrong, you have only to stop and reflect whether a woman of such honesty and intelligence as your good lady, even if she wished to stain your honour in this manner, would ever bring herself to do it before your very eyes. Of myself I say nothing, except that I would sooner allow myself to be drawn and quartered than even contemplate such an act, let alone do it in your presence. Hence it is quite obvious

Youth Everlasting

Ponce de León, who sought the Fountain of Youth (and found Florida), was pursuing another staple of the legend of the lost Golden Age. There is no mistaking the element of sensuality in this quest, as indeed fear of the loss of sexual powers and longing for their restoration are major themes in literature as in mythology. The famous ancient physician Galen concluded (in *De Spermate*) it were better to have no heart than no privates; and Rabelais has Panurge say (in *Gargantua and Pantagruel*): 'When the head is lost, the man is lost, but when the stones are lost, mankind is lost.'

Fig. 1: The Fountain of Youth, *by the Master of the Banderoles, fifteenth century*
Fig. 2: The Old Wives' Mill, *Nuremberg engraving of about 1810.*
Fig. 3: The mythical island of Atlantis, *according to Athanasius Kircher.*
Fig. 4: Idealized rendering of the Field of Ida on Atlantis.

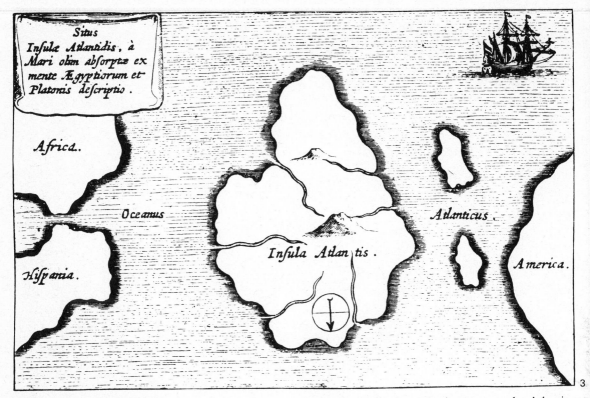

The Lost World

The ancient story of Atlantis goes back to Plato's circumstantial account. It was taken to represent a Golden Age, an ideal state, located somewhere beyond the 'Pillars of Hercules' (the Straits of Gibraltar), and thus gave its name to the Atlantic Ocean beneath which it was believed to have sunk eons ago. The most likely reality behind Atlantis is the volcanic island of Santorini, which is known to have blown up during the earthquakes of *c.* 1550 BC that brought about the collapse of the great Minoan culture of Crete.

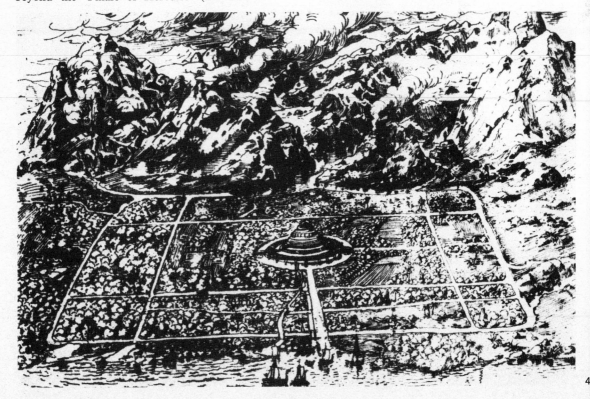

The Garden of Eden – Mankind's Earliest Dream

The ancient legends clustering around the notion of Paradise reached the Babylonians and Assyrians by way of the Gilgamesh epic of the Sumerians. From there they were passed on, in embroidered form, to the Israelites, probably during their Babylonian captivity. But while Adam and Eve, according to the Book of Genesis, enjoyed their naked innocence, primitive man was actually locked in an unending and pitiless struggle with his environment.

The Land of Cockayne – a Burlesque on Paradise

The legend of the lost paradise developed into the idea of Cockayne, the mythical country of super-abundance where nobody needs to work and chicken, ready-fried, flies into people's mouths. Cockayne has been depicted in great detail, with maps showing Beer Island and Drunkards' Lake, the counties of Richlife and Sloth, and villages ranging from Whitefish and Eatwell to Dancefield and Pastime. The picture above was painted by the Flemish master Pieter Bruegel, and now hangs in the Alte Pinakothek in Munich.

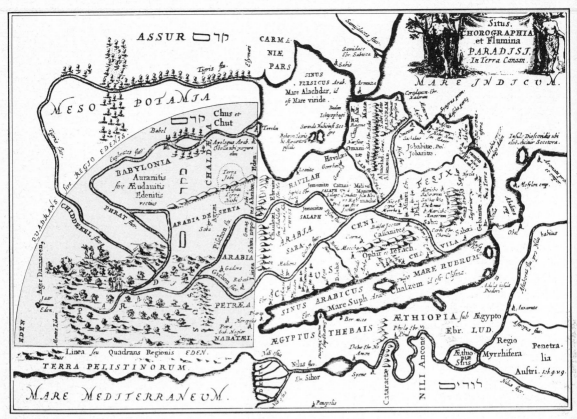

The precise location of Paradise, according to Johann Herbinius, 1678.

The Peaceable Kingdom, *by Matthäus Merian, 1633.*

151

An Oak Tree

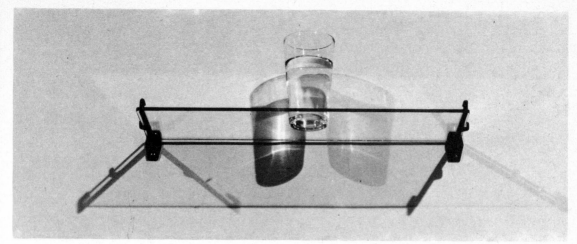

Q: To begin with, could you describe this work?

A: Yes, of course. What I've done is change a glass of water into a full-grown oak tree without altering the accidents of the glass of water.

Q: The accidents?

A: Yes. The colour, feel, weight, size . . . .

Q: Do you mean that the glass of water is a symbol of an oak tree?

A: No. It's not a symbol. I've changed the physical substance of the glass of water into that of an oak tree.

Q: It looks like a glass of water. . . .

A: Of course it does. I didn't change its appearance. But it's not a glass of water. It's an oak tree.

Q: Can you prove what you claim to have done?

A: Well, yes and no. I claim to have maintained the physical form of the glass of water and, as you can see, I have. However, as one normally looks for evidence of physical change in terms of altered form, no such proof exists.

Q: Haven't you simply called this glass of water an oak tree?

A: Absolutely not. It is not a glass of water any more. I have changed its actual substance. It would no longer be accurate to call it a glass of water. One could call it anything one wished but that would not alter the fact that it is an oak tree.

Q: Isn't this just a case of the emperor's new clothes?

A: No. With the emperor's new clothes people claimed to see something which wasn't there because they felt they should. I would be very surprised if anyone told me they saw an oak tree.

Q: Was it difficult to effect the change?

A: No effort at all. But it took me years of work before I realized I could do it.

Q: When precisely did the glass of water become an oak tree?

A: When I put water in the glass.

Q: Does this happen every time you fill a glass with water?

A: No, of course not. Only when I intend to change it into an oak tree.

Q: Then intention causes the change?

A: I would say it precipitates the change.

Q: You don't know how you do it?

A: It contradicts what I feel I know about cause and effect.

Q: It seems to me you are claiming to have worked a miracle. Isn't that the case?

A: I'm flattered that you think so.

Q: But aren't you the only person who can do something like this?

A: How could I know?

Q: Could you teach others to do it?

A: No. It's not something one can teach.

Q: Do you consider that changing the glass of water into an oak tree constitutes an artwork?

A: Yes.

Q: What precisely is the artwork? The glass of water?

A: There is no glass of water any more.

Q: The process of change?

A: There is no process involved in the change.

Q: The oak tree?

A: Yes. The oak tree.

Q: But the oak tree only exists in the mind.

A: No. The actual oak tree is physically present but in the form of the glass of water. As the glass of water was a particular glass of water, the oak tree is also particular. To conceive the category 'oak tree', or to picture a particular oak tree is not to understand and experience what appears to be a glass of water as an oak tree. Just as it is imperceivable, it is also inconceivable.

Q: Did the particular oak tree exist somewhere else before it took the form of the glass of water?

A: No. This particular oak tree did not exist previously. I should also point out that it does not and will not ever have any other form but that of a glass of water.

Q: How long will it continue to be an oak tree?

A: Until I change it.

Michael Craig-Martin, 1973

For me, everyday truth gains its unshakeable character from two elemental events in which idea and appearance on the one hand and truth and reality on the other coincide so strikingly that philosophy and ideology can add nothing. I mean birth and death. I should regard the world as inconsistent, if only the beginning and the end were evident, while everything that happened in between required special interpretation. Logic and reason lead me to the conclusion that joy and sorrow, pleasure and pain, love and hate, chair and table, cat and dog, sun and moon are as true and real as birth and death.

To avoid stultifying naïveté, such blue-eyed Positivism must come to grips with three counter-forces – lies, errors and illusions. We all know that real sounds reaching the ear may convey untruths. 'I love you,' he says, but all he really wants is her money. We must make a distinction here. What is true is that he said to her 'I love you.' But the statement itself may very well be untrue.

Animals too can lie. My dog knows that if he strikes up a sudden bark at night, I will come to see what is the matter. Sometimes nothing is the matter. Having lived with my dog for a long time, I know that he sometimes barks because he wants to draw my attention to something he regards as holding danger for us. But at other times he barks simply because he feels lonely or is afraid. In any event, he realizes: whenever I bark, my human will come.

It is true that most of us fall for lies again and again – but at the same time, lies represent no serious threat to a pragmatic Positivist approach.

Error is an even lesser threat to such an approach, defined as an articulate human response to environmental experience. I regard error as harmless, because it is little more than a temporary breakdown within a system that is, by and large, regarded as real and true. People who think truth cannot be perceived, let alone communicated, can scarcely take a single error very seriously, since, in a manner of speaking, they have enshrined all-pervading error as a fundamental law of the universe.

Very well, then, there remains illusion as a third argument against the seemingly naïve assumption that the world is really as it is perceived by man's senses and stored in his mind after having passed the filter of reason.

Things are not quite so simple in the matter of illusions. In practical terms, they seem innocent enough. Of course we know there are dreams and mirages. Eye and ear seem capable of producing 'perceptions' from within. The blind see nothing and the deaf hear nothing – but the world does not end on that account.

All very well, but nevertheless, the phenomenon of illusion is the most difficult and indigestible problem for the theory of pragmatic Positivism. Personally, I do not think it is all that indigestible, but I'm well aware of the tempting intellectual bridge that leads from the fact that we dream to the conclusion that all life is nothing but a dream. In other words, when we admit that not all subjective perceptions correspond to objective events, do we not imply that it is impossible to distinguish between subjective perceptions and objective events?

What makes illusions so treacherous is their untranslated immediacy. Reason and experience can indirectly unmask lies and errors, but illusions run counter to our basic experience and confuse the view of the world conveyed to us by our senses. Thus the individual has no defences against illusions – at least not at the time he succumbs to them. Usually, of course, he does have further experiences that enable him to apply correctives, just as we do when we wake from a dream – we know it was only an illusion and not real. Yet often enough we need someone else to tell us that we were mistaken, that it was all a dream. Any individual experience may be deceptive, an illusion. As a matter of fact, whole groups of people may collectively believe something to be true that is actually illusory, especially when they influence one another to that effect. And now, to conclude briefly a rather lengthy chain of thought, let it be said that there are no everyday illusions to which all of the people could succumb all of the time, or even most of the people most of the time. For if there were, what may appear to the eccentric to be an everyday illusion would actually be everyday truth.

Münchhausen (Theodor Hosemann)

with a rose rather than a table – and even for a sensitive pragmatist it is not easy to divine what stubborn Idealists and Materialists envisage when they think or speak of a rose.

We should thus have to say, after Gertrude Stein: a table is a table is a table. It is a piece of furniture

The King and Queen of Hearts (Sir John Tenniel).

that is certainly not quite easy to define, built by people all over the world to facilitate some everyday rituals. Doubtless a table does not know it is a table. But the people who build one know very well that that is what they mean to do – make a table. And that a table has various names in various languages should not be an insurmountable obstacle to reflection, even when we do not oversimplify the matter. For it is not just the words that differ, but the meanings too. In some American offices, 'a table' may very well be something on which one puts up one's feet!

The intellectual games philosophers play may have a value of their own. Like chess, they are intriguing and enlightening. But they do have one aspect that should irk us – or at least I think so, perhaps because it irks me personally.

Since we might as well have used a chair as an example instead of a table – or for that matter 'the State' – the Idealist–Materialist obsession with calling everything into question ultimately amounts to an assertion that we simply do not know what exists 'in reality' or 'in truth'.

If I subscribed to this pernicious doctrine, I should

man the barricades and fight for an end to witnesses in court being sworn to tell 'the truth, the whole truth and nothing but the truth'.

What, really, is the meaning of all this scepticism about truth in the world of things, as cultivated by the Idealists, and about the world of man, as secretly nurtured by the Materialists? Rainer Maria Rilke proposed that we probably see things 'as they themselves never inwardly mean to be'. It would not be hard to demonstrate absurdity in the verses of a poet who is not himself absurd at all, but it seems to me to be potentially more rewarding to challenge a discipline that is currently flourishing in the world. I refer to 'Behaviourism', which deals with animals rather than tables.

Animals represent a borderline case between tables and furniture-makers, for they can be credited with neither the awareness of the latter nor the non-awareness of the former (something that might repay closer attention, by the way). Now we ordinary laymen, being only human, seek to comprehend the behaviour of animals in human terms, and are promptly charged by the Behaviourists with the heinous sin of 'anthropomorphism'. We are foolish enough to believe that when a bird pecks at some breadcrumbs in our hand, it trusts us, that when a dog growls, it is angry, and that when a tomcat yowls, it is wooing a mate, in the feline version of a man wooing a woman. The Behaviourists are probably right. The reality of animal life may not be like that at all. But what, then, is 'animal reality'? Let us put it another way. When a dog rolls on its back and waves its legs in the air, who of us can tell, from the point of view of the dog's awareness, whether it is being obsequious or lecherous – or whether it simply wants to play?

We really have no alternative to imputing some form of human 'truth' to animals as to things. The very word 'truth' represents, in my view, a purely human concept that has no acceptable meaning beyond man's own world.

The Good Soldier Schweijk (Josef Lada).

Everyday truth is rather different from the kind of 'truth' that appears in the philosophical systems of the Idealists and Materialists. It is more modest – and also more durable. It is neither more nor less than a proper relation between the environment – the world of things – and human awareness – which, in its own way, clamours for insight.

Everyday Truth

by Rudolf Walter Leonhardt

*Thyl Ulenspiegel and Lamme Goedzak
(Wiltraud Jasper).*

When a philosopher ponders a table too long, strange things happen. If he is a follower of the Idealist School of the German philosopher Kant, he is likely to assure us that we really know nothing about the table's true existence. The table exists only within us, as an idea. We can say nothing about the reality that corresponds to this idea, about this 'thing in itself'. For example, we may be simply dreaming the table, and in that case there would obviously be no reality at all corresponding to the dream table. Dreams are the exemplar *par excellence* of all Idealist philosophers. Oddly enough, the Materialist School, apparently the direct opposite of the Idealist, reaches a quite similar conclusion, for the Materialist too does not rest content with the table's existence. Scientifically founded though the Materialist view is, it is nevertheless rooted in the spirit of our own age and would be difficult to refute within it. That which we call a 'table', thus runs the argument, more or less, is 'in reality' not a mere idea – for of course the Materialist wishes to cling to his matter, his material – but a conglomeration of molecular events received by the radar system of our senses and conducted by our nerves to the computer of our brain which, since we are appropriately programmed, signals 'table, table, table', together with some additional information concerning the table's colour, size, shape and position. In the end, the table of a strict Materialist is not much different from the table idea of the Idealist – with one important exception: the Materialist, as a physicist, insists that he is able to know and describe precisely the 'thing in itself'. He tells us, however, that he can do this only with the help of a special language of physics, consisting in the main of equations, which a normal person like you or I cannot comprehend.

Materialist and Idealist thinkers, in other words, are in full agreement that it is impossible to tell the truth about a table in such a way that anyone can understand it.

To be sure, if it were only a matter of setting the table for dinner, of laying out plates and cutlery, we could begin by saying that the table is simply a table – and get the approval of Idealist and Materialist philosophers. We would describe it as a level area raised above the floor on legs and intended for dining, writing or playing cards.

But even people who deal with tables solely on an everyday rather than a philosophical basis are likely to find that in the end it is not all that easy to say what we mean when we pronounce the word 'table'. Is it really nothing more than 'a level area raised above the floor on legs'? After all, there are tables that fold down out of the wall. Is that still a 'table' or has it stopped being one? And what about a Japanese table? The Japanese squat on the floor, and where there are no chairs, there cannot very well be a table. Some Japanese, however, like to sit like Europeans and 'cheat' a little. They dig holes for the legs into the floor and then actually 'sit at table', although they are sitting at floor level. Does a hollowed-out floor constitute a 'table'? You see, we get into plenty of trouble even without the philosophers and physicists.

And we certainly do not need the linguists! They will come and tell us that a table, real or not, is not a table everywhere. In French it will be *une table* and in German *ein Tisch*. We will not even ask what it is called in Tokyo, for that might cause additional difficulties, as we have seen.

Gertrude Stein said something about roses. Her profound statement is a kind of double slap, and I should like to apply it to our table, hitting the inveterate Idealist with the palm and the equally uncompromising Materialist with the back of the hand. Otherwise I should have had to start this entire parable

Don Quixote and Sancho Panza (Gerhart Kraaz).

Man's ideas of his gods are always relative. The Ethiopians of Africa envisage their gods as black and snub-nosed, the people of Thrace as blue-eyed and red-haired. If cattle or lions possessed hands fit for shaping figures, the gods they would mould would look like cattle or lions.

XENOPHANES

A man went up to a mountain and said: 'What a fool thou art, O Mountain! Thou knowest neither thy size nor thy height nor thy configuration. I on the other hand know everything about thee.' The mountain pondered a while and then said: 'It is true that I know none of this; but *I am the mountain!*'

INDIAN FABLE

A wolf caught sight of some herdsmen feasting on lamb in their shelter. 'What a fuss you would make,' quoth he as he drew nearer, 'if I were doing such a thing!'

THE FABLES OF AESOP

All enchantment entails partial identification with the enchanted – whom I can compel to see a thing, to believe in it, to feel it, as I wish.

NOVALIS

Acknowledgments

(p.15) 'Diamond cut Diamond' by
Ewart Milne, Bodley Head, London;
(p.33) 'The Impossible Fact',
translated by Max Knight, University
of California Press, Berkeley, Calif.,
1963; (p.68) 'Fooling the Skin', text
and drawings adapted from *Insight*,
Portland Publications, London;
(p.78) 'The Apocryphal Dialogue of
Xymmachus', after Plato, translated
from Robert Neumann, *Mit fremden
Federn, Der Parodien erster Band*,
Ullstein-Verlag, Frankfurt and
Berlin, 1969; (p.87) Geo-Metric
Verse, by Willard R. Esprey, A.S.
Barnes & Co. Inc., Cranbury, NJ;
(p.89) 'The Man Who Carried His
Hat' by Carlo Manzoni, translated
from *Die Lügengeschichten des Carlo
Manzoni*, Deutscher Taschenbuch-
verlag, Munich, 1973; (p.118)
'Bifocal Trouble' by Edgar A.
Guest, from *Life's Highway*, 1933,
published in *A Gross of Green
Spectacles*, Hatton Press, London,
1951; (pp.132/133) Plato Epistle VII,
translated by R. G. Bury, Loeb
Classical Library, Heinemann,
London/Harvard, Cambridge, Mass.;
(pp.144/145) 'The Elusive Rings of
Saturn', adapted from *Insight*,
Portland Publications, London.

Bibliography

A. ARNAU, *Kunst der Fälscher –
Fälscher der Kunst*, Düsseldorf 1969
CARRAHER/THURSTON, *Optical
Illusions and the Visual Arts*, New
York 1966
T. N. CORNSWEET, *Visual Perception*,
London 1970
U. EBBECKE, *Wirklichkeit und
Täuschung*, Göttingen 1956
M. C. ESCHER, *Graphik und
Zeichnungen*, Munich 1962
K. GENTIL, *Optische Täuschungen*,
Cologne 1967
E. H. GOMBRICH, *Art and Illusion*,
London 1972
R. L. GREGORY, *Eye and Brain*,
London 1966
– AND E. H. GOMBRICH, *Illusion in
Nature and Art*, London 1973

B. JULESZ, *Foundations of
Cyclopian Perception*, Chicago
1971
F. KAHN, *Das Leben des Menschen*,
Stuttgart 1931
M. LUCKIESH, *Visual Illusions*,
London 1922
W. METZGER, *Gesetze des Sehens*,
Frankfurt/M 1953
J. REICHARDT, *Cybernetic Serendipity*,
New York 1969
R. RICHARDSON, *Mental Imagery*,
London 1969
H. SCHOBER, *Sehen*, Frankfurt/M
1973
E. STRAUSS, *Vom Sinne der Sinne*,
Berlin 1956
S. TOLANSKY, *Optical Illusions*,
Oxford 1956

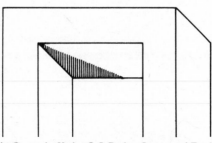

Library of Congress Catalog Card Number: 77–71375

ISBN: Hardbound 0–03–020891–2
Paperback 0–03–020886–6

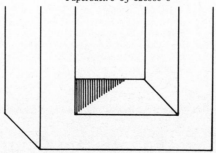

Picture Credits

ADAGP, Paris + Cosmopress, Geneva 10 22 82 93 100
Verlag Amstutz & Herdeg, Zurich 32
Heather Angel 39
Frank Arnau, *Kunst der Fälscher – Fälscher der Kunst*, Econ Verlag GmbH, Düsseldorf 143
Emil Bachmann, *Wer hat Himmel und Erde gemessen?*, Otto Verlag, Thun 121
M. Barry in British *Reader's Digest*, July 1975 10
Bayerische Staatsgemälde-sammlungen, Munich 150
Albert Bettex, Thalwil 130 131
Galerie Beyeler, Basle 21
Bibliothèque Nationale, Paris 42 134
Georg Bischof, Steinhausen 93
Werner Bischof/Magnum 38
Brigitte, Gruner + Jahr AG & Co., Munich 85
British Museum, London 94
Brookhaven National Laboratory 16
Büchergilde Gutenberg, 133 155
Sammlung E. G. Bührle, Zurich 27
Zdeněk Burian, *Prehistoric Man*, Artia Verlag, Prague 119
Camera Press Ltd, London 140
Ronald G. Carraher, Jacqueline B. Thurston, *Optical Illusions and the Visual Arts*, Reinhold Inc., New York 54 91 112 113
Franz Coray, Lucerne 11 12 90 131
Christopher Davies 33
Dilia, Prague 154
Lo Duca, *La Technique de l'Erotisme*, Jean-Jacques Pauvert, Paris 82
Ulrich Ebbecke, *Wirklichkeit und Täuschung*, Vandenhoek & Ruprecht, Göttingen 108
Eltern, Gruner + Jahr AG & Co., Munich 29
Escher Foundation, Haags Gemeentemuseum, The Hague 76
Ralph M. Evans, *Eye, Film and Camera in Color Photography*, J. Wiley, Inc., New York 96
Jean-Claude Forest, *Barbarella II*, Wilhelm Heyne Verlag, Munich 146
Bamber Gascoigne, *World Theatre* 144
Karl Gentil, *Optische Täuschungen*, Aulis Verlag Deubner & Co. KG, Cologne, 101

E. H. Gombrich, *Art and Illusion*, Phaidon Press Ltd, London 126
R. L. Gregory, *Eye and Brain*, Weidenfeld & Nicolson Ltd, London 65 66 92 116
Karl Gruber, *Die Gestalt der deutschen Stadt*, Verlag Georg D. W. Callwey, Munich 24
Gebrüder Paul und Kurt Gysi, Erlenbach 72 73
Werner de Haas, Fredi Knorr, *Was lebt im Meer?*, Kosmos Verlag, Stuttgart 131
Ingeborg Hägg-Jacobsson, Kode 39 66 67
Fred Hentschel, Lucerne 31
Hobby – das Magazin der Technik, Ehapa Verlag GmbH, Stuttgart 52
Illustrations- und Photopress, Zurich 23
Imprécis d'Erotisme, Jean-Jacques Pauvert, Paris 112
Insel-Verlag, Frankfurt/M 146
Fritz Kahn, *Der Mensch*, Albert Müller Verlag, Rüschlikon 58
Fritz Kahn, *Knaurs Buch vom menschlichen Körper*, Droemersche Verlagsanstalt Th. Knaur Nachf., Munich 69 109
H. B. D. Kettlewell 39
Bernhard W. Kieser, Meerbusch 49
Ruth Koser-Michaels, *Andersen Märchen*, Droemersche Verlagsanstalt Th. Knaur Nachf. 142
Walter Linsenmaier 37
Konrad Lorenz, *Seewiesen* 117
Mad, E. C. Publications Inc., New York 84 98 99
Magnum, Verlag M. Dumont Schauberg, Cologne 16 20 44
Hans Marcus, Buch- und Kunst-antiquariat, Düsseldorf 39
Kevin MacDonnell, *Edward Muybridge*, Weidenfeld & Nicolson, Ltd., London 64
E. McQuillan 27
Robert Michel 64
Migros Genossenschaftsbund, Zurich 132
Heinz Moos Verlag GmbH & Co., KG, Gräfelfing 34 35 95 101 103
Natural History Photographic Agency, Westerham, Kent 36
Newsweek, New York 86

Penfield and Rasmussen, *The Cerebral Codex of Man*, Macmillan Inc., New York 107
Peynet 42
Quick, Heinrich Bauer Verlag, Munich 41 117
H. Georg Rauch, Hamburg 81 124
Jasia Reichardt, *Cybernetic Serendipity*, Praeger Inc., New York 18 19 72 83
Rowan Gallery, London 152
Rundschau, Ciba-Geigy AG, Basle 100
Robert Schenk and Georg Schmidt, *Kunst und Naturform*, Basilius-Presse, AG, Basle 21
Herbert Schober, *Das Sehen*, VEB Fachbuchverlag, Leipzig 83 86 101
Schweizerische Allgemeine Volks-Zeitung, Ringier & Co, AG, Zofingen 102
Schweizerisches Sozialarchiv, Zurich 138 139
Schweizerische Verkehrszentrale/Ph. Giegel, Zurich 64
Spadem, Paris + Cosmopress, Geneva 21 32
Daniel Spoerri, Düsseldorf 75
Sport, Jean Frey AG, Zurich 97
Staatliche Hochschule für bildende Künste, Hamburg 14
Kurt Stampfli, Berne 102
Otto Steinert, Essen 28
Tate Gallery, London 26 33
Richard Taylor 42 118
Time Life Inc., New York 20 24 29 116
J. v. Uexküll, G. K. Kriszat, *Streifzüge durch die Umwelt von Tieren und Menschen*, Julius Springer, Berlin 15
Unesco Courier, UNESCO, Paris 24 45 57 85 97
A. Paul Weber 126
John Rowan Wilson, *The Mind*, Time Inc., New York 115
Die Zeit, Zeit-Verlag GmbH AG, Hamburg 121

All illustrations not credited above come from the studios of E. and R. Lanners, Zurich, and C. J. Bucher, Lucerne

ABOUT THIS BOOK

Only a few decades ago, we still believed science could explain the 'how' of everything. Today we face the question of whether we are even in touch with reality, or ever can be. Thinkers and philosophers have become convinced that the objects of our world merely represent the sum of their properties for us and that these qualities exist solely in our consciousness. What we perceive is the result of a thinking process, a kind of natural magic, that conjures up within us a sensation of the object seen, while at the same time suggesting to us a belief in its reality. Perhaps the greatest illusion is the way we take it for granted that the real world 'out there' coincides with what we optically perceive as 'real'. The image we create of our environment is purely human and subjective, hence one-sided. A dog's image of the world, or that of a bee or a bird, is quite different. Every living creature is equipped with different organs, receives impressions altogether different from ours, and these images are integrated in utterly different fashion, in the differently organized brains nature has provided. Everyone really feels, hears, sees only in his brain, in his own peculiar and mysterious fashion. Oddly enough, we tend to give little thought to the machinery with which we think and feel, build up our lives, create our view of the world, take our decisions. We fail to appreciate that this machinery not only remains an unsolved puzzle, but all too often succumbs to error, is swayed by prejudice, gives way to illusions. Is illusion merely a superficial represent- ation of the world, just a figment in practical life? Or is it an amusing form of self-deception that takes the place of a sober look at the facts? When we critically examine the 'mechanism' of illusion, the in- sight we thus gain into our weaknesses, rather than 'disillusion' us, is likely to exert a certain fascination, especially when we come to realize that de- spite our awareness that we are victims of illusion, we are unable to avoid suc- cumbing to it. Illusion, further- more, need not be considered solely as deception and falsification, for it represents at the same time the fundamental creative principle, the motive that impels us to change the world along the lines of our dreams. Hence delving into illusion and error is more than merely entertaining. It may stimulate us to engage in original reflection and fruitful meditation.

Illusions

Edited by EDI LANNERS

Translated and adapted by Heinz Norden

Holt, Rinehart and Winston · New York

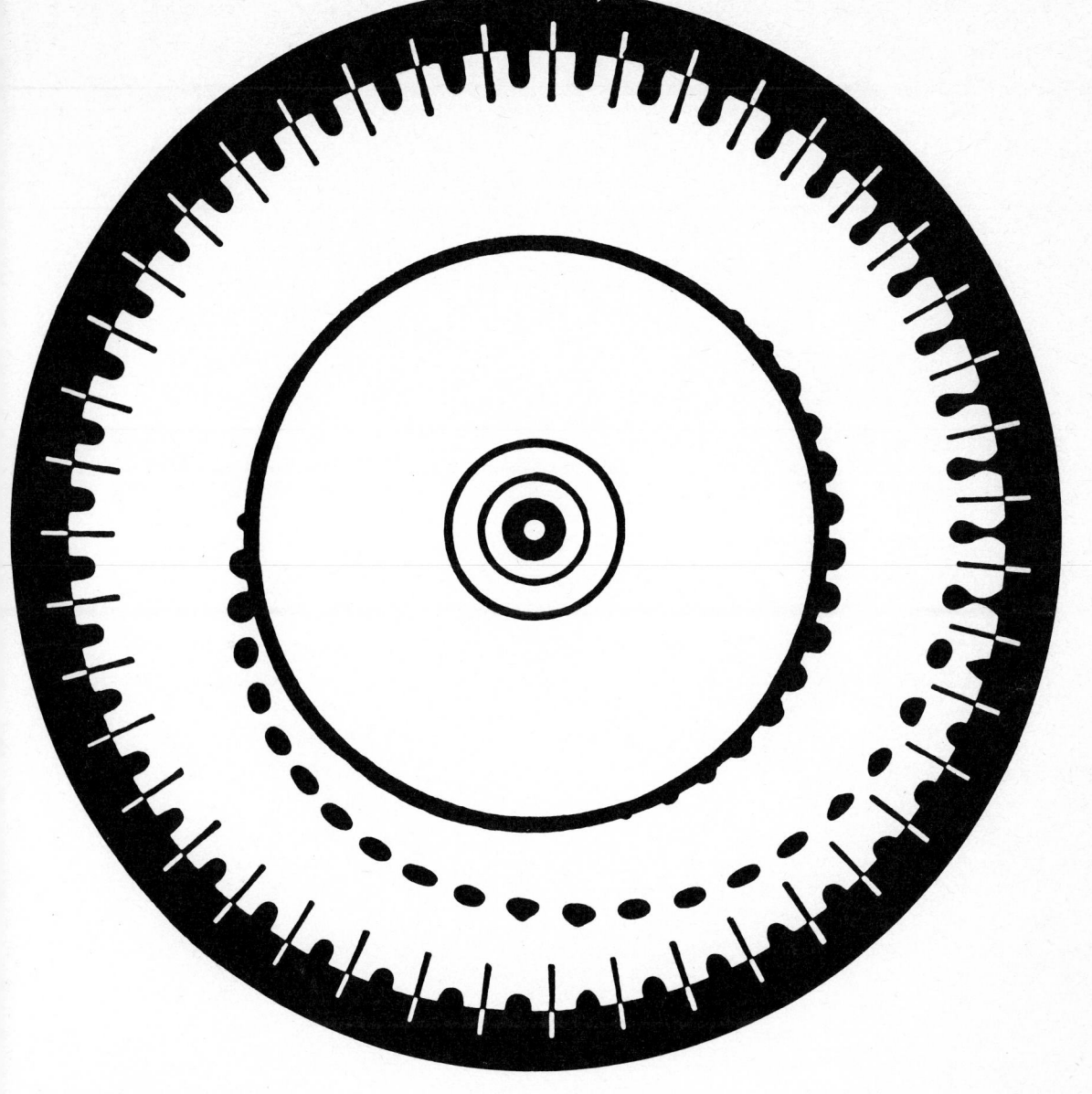

The Falling Drop

Cut out the circle and paste it on a cardboard circle about 1½ in. larger in diameter. Next cut out the white centre dot and the slots round the edge (marked in black and white). Now glue the unprinted side to an empty cotton-spool with the holes coinciding precisely. Put a stick of the right size loosely through both holes and fix a button to one end to keep the disc from falling off. Wind a light string round the spool and pull it off to set the disc spinning. Look at the mirror image of the marked side through the slots from the unprinted side. You should see what looks quite realistically like a falling drop. If the image is indistinct, widen the slots.

Figures at the Bottom of p. A1:

Cut out the three pictures but do not separate the two horsemen. You will find it impossible to assemble the four figures in such a way that the two horsemen are seated correctly on their mounts.

Colour Discs

Cut out these patterned discs and mount them centrally on larger (record-size) discs of heavy cardboard. Then spin them under a strong light on a turntable with adjustable rpm, increasing the speed of rotation.

The grey tones will slowly take on colour of astonishing luminosity. The phenomenon will be observed even under monochromatic light. This is not a case of the white light being separated into its component colour spectrum, but a central eye—brain phenomenon.

A 3

The Spiral Mystery

When this spiral is spun about its white centre, it seems to shrink or to expand, depending on the direction of rotation. When we have gazed at the disc spinning at moderate speed for some ten to twenty seconds and then look fixedly at a single object, that object will seem to expand or shrink, in a direction opposite to that of the spiral.

This illusion cannot be caused by eye movement, since the changes in size of the lamp or ash tray or whatever seem to take place quite paradoxically in all directions, without our having to change our own position in the least.

Our eyes seem to be 'defending' themselves when they are forced to look at such a vortex for any length of time. They seem to 'shift into reverse', so to speak. If we suddenly black out the rotating spiral, our brain will not respond instantly but retain its oppositional bias for several seconds.